THE BIOLOGY OF HUMAN INTELLIGENCE

Proceedings of the Twentieth Annual Symposium of the Eugenics Society London, 1983.

Edited by:

C.J. TURNER

Department of Human Biology and Health, University of Surrey, Guildford, Surrey

H.B MILES

Department of Zoology, The University, Hull

General Editor:

ROBERT CHESTER

Department of Social Administration, The University, Hull

1984

Published for THE EUGENICS SOCIETY
by Nafferton Books Limited
Nafferton, Driffield, North Humberside

THE EUGENICS SOCIETY
69 Eccleston Square,
London, SW1V 1PJ.

British Library Cataloguing in Publication Data

Eugenics Society. Annual Conference (20th: 1983: London)
The Biology of Human Intelligence
1. Biology 2. Human Intelligence
I. Title II. Turner, C.J. III. Miles, H.B.

ISBN 0-905484-45-2

This book is dedicated to

ELIOT SLATER
CBE, MA, MD, FRCP, DPM

1904-1983

Contents

Contributors

C.R. BRAND, Department of Psychology, University of Edinburgh, 7 George Square, Edinburgh EH8 9JZ, Scotland.

H.J. EYSENCK, Institute of Psychiatry, University of London, De Crespigny Park, Denmark Hill, London SE5 8AF.

Glenda FREDMAN, Department of Child Psychiatry, Institute of Child Health, Hospital for Sick Children, Great Ormond Street, London WC1N 3JH.

Joan FREEMAN, Department of Education, University of Manchester, Oxford Road, Manchester M13 9PL.

P. GRAHAM, Department of Child Psychiatry, Institute of Child Health, Hospital for Sick Children, Great Ormond Street, London, WC1N 3JH.

J.K. HEWITT, Department of Psychology, University of Birmingham, Birmingham B15 2TT.

R.M.C. HUNTLEY, Department of Developmental Paediatrics, The Wolfson Centre, Institute of Child Health, Mecklenburgh Square, London WC1N 2AP.

Krystina A. LAST, Department of Genetics, University of Birmingham, Birmingham B15 2TT.

G.C.N. MASCIE-TAYLOR, Department of Physical Anthropology, University of Cambridge, Downing Street, Cambridge CB2 3DZ.

Vivienne McLOUGHLIN, Department of Child Psychiatry, Institute of Child Health, Hospital for Sick Children, Great Ormond Street, London WC1N 3JH.

M.J. SHAYER, Centre for Science and Mathematics Education, Chelsea College, Bridges Place, London SW6 4HR.

J.E. STEVENSON, Department of Psychology, University of Surrey, Guildford GU2 5XH.

B. STRATFORD, School of Education, University of Nottingham, University Park, Nottingham NH7 2RD.

M.J. WATERHOUSE, Faculty of Arts, Gwent College of Higher Education, Clarence Place, Newport, Gwent NPT OUW, Wales.

J. WILLIAMS, Centre for Science and Mathematics Education, Chelsea College, Bridges Place, London SW6 4HR.

Preface

The application of human intelligence to the study of itself has necessarily always been an enterprise fraught with methodological hazard and philosophical circularity. These considerations came to the fore during the 1970's when, fuelled by the nature-nurture debate in the parallel field of sociobiology, frustration surfaced and the course of scientific discussion in psychology and genetics was disturbed by emotional, political and ideological interpolation. The ensuing disputes, which were sometimes personally directed, and frequently acrimonious, did however serve a purpose in stimulating new patterns of thinking about the nature, definition and measurement of intelligence. In response to generally held conclusions about the heritability of intelligence, research began afresh based on the application of more sensitive and sophisticated methods to more carefully selected collections of data. Such work served not only to re-establish the reputability of genetic studies but also to focus general attention on the search for the fundamental biological processes which underlie cognitive behaviour and which might be identified in measurable form as constitutional determinants of variability in individual performance. As the lessons of the disputes were assimilated, there was an inclination to re-examine, perhaps with more open minds than before, the purpose and usefulness of knowledge about individual intellectual capacity. Recognising the significance of these developments, and the importance of bringing them to the attention of a wider public, the Council of the Eugenics Society sponsored in September 1983 a Symposium on 'The Biology of Human Intelligence'. This book contains the majority of the papers presented on that occasion, describing recent research work and ideas about the measurement and inheritance of intelligence in a broad biological context and in a framework of human social and educational relevance.

In the first chapter, Martin Waterhouse provides a broad introduction to the subject by describing the chief components of intelligent behaviour as they can be identified hierarchically in primate animals set in a evolutionary sequence leading to man. Dr. Michael Shayer and John Williams introduce a further biological dimension to the book, a physiological one, by postulating on adolescent growth spurt in the development of certain intellectual abilities analogous to that characteristic of physical growth. These considerations set the scene for Professor Hans Eysenck who, in his Galton Lecture, discusses rival conceptions of the nature of human intelligence and its operational definition. He concludes in favour of the validity of the notion of intelligence as a general factor underlying other cognitive functions, a factor which is measurable, largely heritable, and essentially physiological in its operation. He points out, fittingly, that this view represents a revolution in psychological thinking, a revolution which takes us back to the view and approach pioneered by Sir Francis Galton a century ago as one of the most influential founders of the eugenics movement and of the Eugenics Society.

One of the physiological approaches to the measurement of intelligence cited by Professor Eysenck is dealt with in more detail by Chris Brand in his paper on intelligence and inspection times. The heritability issue is tackled by Drs. John Hewitt and Krystina Last who present material on the IQ scores of twins, and by Jim Stevenson and colleagues who also employ twin data in their investigation of reading disability. Both contributions demonstrate that the methods of geneticists are not crudely reductionist, but through their resolving power are capable of raising fresh questions which heighten our appreciation of the many factors which influence behaviour and achievement.

Such a conclusion also derives from Dr. Nick Mascie-Taylor's demonstration of the many biological and social factors which can be shown to be variously correlated with IQ score. The later chapters in the book deal with areas where our understanding of mental functioning influences our attitude to particular groups and individuals in the population. Dr. Brian Stratford shows how research findings about the specific disabilities of Down's syndrome children can have useful implications for the upbringing and education of such children, and Dr. Joan Freeman reports on the Gulbenkian Project on Gifted Children. Finally, Dr. Michael Huntley discusses the problems faced by families where one member is not necessarily retarded or gifted to an abnormal degree, but is merely different — exceptional in the context of that particular family. His contribution reminds us that individual variation in intellectual capacity and achievement is a fact of every-day human life: the problems which arise may be mundane but their humane solution depends upon everyone's increasing understanding and knowledge.

C.J. Turner
H.B. Miles

Editors' Note

At the Symposium, papers were also presented by Drs. A.E. and D.E. Hendrickson on 'The Biological Basis of Individual Differences in Intelligence', and by Professor R. Lynn on 'Racial and Ethnic Differences in Intelligence', which unfortunately were not available for publication in a form appropriate to this volume.

A full account of the Hendricksons' work, to which they referred, has been published in 'A Model for Intelligence', edited by H.J. Eysenck (1982), published by Springer-Verlag.

Acknowledgements

Thanks are due to Professor Margaret Sutherland and to the late Professor Cedric Carter, who helped and advised on the content and speakers for the symposium; also to Miss Eileen Walters, General Secretary of the Eugenics Society, who made the arrangements for the Symposium and assisted in the preparation of the manuscripts for publication.

Problem Solving Primates: Aspects of the Evolution of Intelligence

MARTIN WATERHOUSE

Gwent College of Higher Education, Newport, Gwent, Wales

In a short story, 'Man of the Year Million', H.G. Wells described the future evolution of *Homo sapiens* in which the creature we know today has been replaced by one which specialises in reason and dexterity, quite unemotional, and with a morphology which reflects these traits: a huge brain, a large hand, and little else. Wells writes:

> 'And so at last comes a vision of earthly cherubim, hopping heads, great unemotional intelligence, and little hearts, fighting together perforce and fiercely against the cold that grips them tighter and tighter' (1972, p.134).

In his introduction to the story, Wells argues that man of the distant future is far more interesting than man of the past. With this it is necessary to disagree. If we wish to understand the nature of intelligence, its potentialities and constraints, we need to know how it evolved. As Koestler (1969) has noted, we are an 'evolutionary package deal', and as far as intelligence is concerned, we should be aware that the 'wiseness' of *Homo sapiens sapiens* (modern man) is contingent on our evolutionary history. I prefer, therefore, to take the advice of the king at the trial in 'Alice in Wonderland':

> 'Begin at the beginning', the king said gravely, 'and go on till you come to the end; then stop'.

At a conference on the biology of human intelligence this is good advice, and as an ethologist and anthropologist interested in the evolution of human behaviour the beginning must lie in the behaviour of non-human animal species, particularly in the instinctive behaviour of the lower animals.

I will first give a brief introduction to the ethological study of behaviour. Much of this discussion will deal with the fixed action patterns of animals: these are unlearnt, occur in highly specific contexts and are highly predictable; they are also functionally related to the survival needs of the animal. At the very least this discussion will be a neat contrast to the intelligent behaviour of higher primates, including man, but even at this level it may be possible to tease out elements of behaviour which cannot be easily interpreted as instinctive, but involve learning, and a flexible form of behaviour — exploration — typical of the young of some species and of adults investigating a new environment. When I come to discuss primates however, it will become obvious that many of the inflexible behaviour patterns which have been studied and conceptualised by ethologists such as Huxley (1914), Lorenz (1967), and Tinbergen (1951) just do not occur: behaviour is more flexible, there is neo-cortical control over behaviour and the animals may even devise strategies. Once again it may be possible to tease out elements which throw light on the origins of intelligence.

Finally, man's closest living relative, the chimpanzee, must be looked at very closely indeed. Recent research reviewed by Tanner (1981) in molecular biology emphasises this relationship which was first stressed by Thomas Huxley in 1863 when he compared the anatomies of various non-human primates with *Homo sapiens.* Psychological and ethological studies have also established a close link between the two species. The problem-solving experiments of Köhler are well-known, as are the attempts by Premack and the Gardners to teach chimpanzees to speak (Linden, 1976). In the wild, Goodall (1971) has observed chimpanzees fabricating crude implements to gain a scarce resource, and at the London Zoo, Morris' experiments and observations led him to conclude that chimpanzees were capable of aesthetic response (1964). More recently, Menzel (1972) has observed the cooperative use of 'tools' to solve problems, and de Waal (1982) claims that the social environment of chimpanzees favours calculating, strategy-making and controlled animals who are able to form coalitions in their bids for dominance. Observations such as these now make it difficult for anthropologists to sustain their definitions of man's uniqueness as a tool-making (Oakley, 1956), language generating (Linden, 1976), or culture-producing (Hoebel, 1960) animal. Indeed, some of de Waal's observations suggest that the chimpanzee may even have a conception of 'self' (see also Shafton, 1976).

Darwinism and Behaviour

It should be stressed that the comparative study of intelligence was only possible in a post Darwinian atmosphere in which the animal/man, instinct/intelligence dichotomies were breaking down. In 1860 the exponents of the Darwin-Wallace theory of natural selection had battled with their theological opposite numbers for the 'soul' of man. Darwin's book, written in the previous year, had been devoted to the possibility of a mechanism of change in non-human species (a teleology without divinity) which was later used to understand *Homo sapiens.* 'The Origin of Species' has little to say about intelligence although chapter 8 attacks the view of the dominant school of 'Natural Theologians' who were content to divide man and animal along the instinct/reason boundary.

Darwin was concerned to demonstrate that instinct was due to natural selection but he does add:

> 'a little dose of judgement or reason . . . often comes into play . . .' (1962, p.244).

In his short work on earthworms Darwin suggests:

> 'If worms have the power of acquiring some notion, however rude, of the shape of an object and their burrows, as seems to be the case, they deserve to be called intelligent; for they then act in nearly the same manner as would a man under similar circumstance'. (1945, p.58).

I suspect that he was underestimating the complexity of instinct in this particular case but the important point is that, for Darwin, intelligence is not something 'super-added' and unique to man, a view which was not only held by the Natural Theologians but one which has its roots deep in Western culture (see, for example, Ryle, 1963 and Beach, 1961). Descartes gives a good re-statement of the argument:

> 'After the error of atheism there is nothing that leads weak minds further astray from the paths of virtue than that the minds of other animals resemble our own, and that therefore we have no greater right to future life than have gnats and ants' (quoted Beach 1961, p.167).

The soul was the problem and Beach has located it as central to the man/animal dichotomy. Christianity, in its stress on the existence of a soul and life after death, presupposed a choice between good and evil; animals do not have souls and therefore do not need to make rational choices. As the theological position has waned it has been replaced by other dichotomies devised by anthropologists and sociologists. Fortunately, the unique observations on the chimpanzee referred to earlier now make such views less tenable.

The Ethological Study of Behaviour

Oddly enough, the comparative study of animal behaviour — ethology — hardly deals with the study of intelligence although it is based firmly on Darwinian principles. This is a pity as it has meant that the study of intelligence has developed largely without the evolutionary insight and critical methodology of the ethologist. The reason is in part historical: the founding fatners of the discipline concentrated their studies on birds, fish and insects where it is possible to build up an explanatory framework without recourse to concepts such as intelligence. However, the insights gained in this research give a useful counterpoint to my later discussion of intelligence.

The research of the Dutch ethologist Tinbergen is a model of ethological method; there is the patient, time-consuming observation of animals in the wild, the careful noting and description of behaviour patterns and an ingenious array of field experiments which clarify the mechanisms behind the behaviour and give some indication of the perceptual field of the animal (e.g. Tinbergen, 1951, 1974). In an early series of field observations made along the sandy wastes of the Dutch coast, Tinbergen (1974) and his colleagues unravelled the behaviour of the predatory wasp *Philanthus.* This wasp digs out holes and chambers in the sand in which it deposits eggs which must be kept fed on the bodies of honey bees. Tinbergen's many research questions included: how does the wasp find and kill its prey and how was it able to identify its burrow on returning from the hunt? *Philanthus* has the ability to identify its prey (the honey bee) from amongst the many airborne insects, some of which mimic the colouration of the honey bee. Tinbergen, initially, did not even know which sense, sight, smell, touch or sound was being utilised. However, two early observations were important. He noted that when a wasp was forced to drop its prey it would always approach downwind of it when attempting to retrieve it, suggesting the importance of smell. In an experimental situation when a wasp and a honey bee were imprisoned together in a glass jar, the wasp only seized the bee after its antennae had been touched by the bee — this appeared to trigger off the full hunting sequence which was only satiated after the bee had been stung, grasped firmly and squeezed so that nectar trickled from its mouth. After the nectar had been eaten by the wasp it transported its prey back to the nest. Careful observation in the natural environment showed that there is an initial phase in which a potential prey is located visually, the wasp then orients itself downwind of the prey and checks the scent. The importance of scent can be tested by a series of experiments in which dummy bees are presented to the wasp: a freshly killed bee, a scented piece of wood and a deodorised bee. All dummies are 'hovered at', but only those which smell are captured; thus a scented piece of wood is preferable to a deodorised bee. However, although the piece of wood is captured it is not stung because another trigger mechanism is required, a tactile one, which the wasp does not receive in this case. Other experiments show that this behaviour is highly stereotyped and must follow an inflexible sequence of events.

Such a behavioural sequence would seem typical of much of behaviour of lower animals: it is a rigid and inflexible, albeit complicated, structure. It does not mean however that all behaviour is equally rigid. There appear to be sets of behaviour which require an element of learning for satisfactory completion. In the early stages of his research, Tinbergen was interested in the ability of his wasps to find their burrows on return. He observed that on leaving the burrow the wasp would perform a 'locality study', circling above the burrow before flying off in search of prey. Tinbergen was able to show that the wasps were learning about their environment: they were reacting to particular visual stimuli in the vicinity of the burrow. Certain types of objects and certain configurations of objects provided an optimum learning situation. The wasps responded to hemispheres rather than flat discs, tall objects rather than small, dented objects rather than smooth. They were also reacting to a gestalt: objects arranged in a circle were preferred to those arranged in a square or a triangle. Most of this evidence was collected by the simple expedient of placing various shaped objects, in various patterns, around the nest, and when the wasp departed having made its 'locality study', moving some or all of the objects to a new location nearby. The wasps were invariably 'fooled' when the critical objects were moved and would attempt to locate their nests in the new location. This 'fooling' of the animal is a basic ethological technique and has proved successful in showing which parts of a stimulus configuration trigger off a reaction; thus, male sticklebacks primed by hormonal changes which occur during the breeding season can be made to perform complex sequences of mating behaviour when presented with crude dummies of females with swollen bellies, whereas they will not respond to life-like dummies without the protruberance. Herring gull chicks will beg when presented with a piece of card roughly in the shape of an adult's beak.

The behaviour of animals in their natural habitats seems well-honed and is explicable in terms of natural selection but it is automatic, and dependent on a complicated series of external and internal stimuli which trigger appropriate behaviour. It is only in the laboratory that the limitations of such genetic programming become obvious. This is exemplified in an experiment performed by W.M.S. Russell (Russell and Russell, 1961) on the South American clawed frog. The reproductive strategy of the male frog works well enough in the wild: as the breeding season develops, the male must not pass up any opportunity to impregnate an ovulating female if he is to succeed in the evolutionary stakes, but neither must he waste too much time courting non-ovulating females. The evolutionary strategy is simple and is programmed accordingly: (1) clasp any object which is shaped roughly like a female. In practice the frog may end up clasping another male, a non-ovulating female, a tree branch, or, if he is lucky, a receptive female; (2) if it is a non-ovulating female a negative stimulus is emitted, as it is if it is a male that is clasped, the frog unclasps and swims away and little time has been wasted. It is a simple behavioural strategy which works, but not when confronted by the ethologist! In one of his experiments, Russell placed a male frog in an aquarium with a non-ovulating female, the male clasped the female who emitted the negative stimulus (a 'tut tut' sound). He unclasped and swam away looking for a more receptive female and, of course, encountered the same female who made the same response.This behaviour carried on for the twelve hours the experiment lasted; it was the human experimenter, not the male frog, who tired first. In the wild the strategy is reasonable but in the experiment there was not the slightest indication that the frog ever learnt by its mistake. Its behaviour consisted of two acts: clasp (and continue the sequence if the response is favourable) and unclasp (if the response is unfavourable). The two acts were quite independent of each other and there was no evidence of a higher level of integration which is the hallmark of learning or intelligence mechanisms.

This will have to suffice as an introduction to the ethological study of behaviour. As long as it is understood that 'instinct' and 'innate' are only first approximations to an understanding of what may be highly complex series of events, they seem to be useful concepts and highlight the fact that dependence on genetic information produces limited and highly rigid patterns of behaviour which do not allow individual animals to adapt to change. As we have seen however, in the case of the 'location studies' made by *Philanthus,* even within the 'instinct system' there may be room for adaptive modification by the individual. In the process of evolution there has been a gradual emancipation so that by the time the higher primates are reached:

> 'the inbuilt chunks of information can operate only as reliable nodes around which more highly integrated perceptions take form'. (Shafton, 1976, p.9).

Exploration and Learning

The concept of learning has the same sort of imprecision about it as instinct but it is a useful shorthand for such mechanisms as imprinting, imitation, trial-and-error, and classic conditioning. Mechanisms such as these provide extra-genetic information which allows individual animals to modify behaviour. It is most characteristic of species which may be termed opportunist: they tend to be structurally generalised, unconfined to a specific ecological niche and have a diverse repertoire of responses. Morris (1964) has characterised species along a continuum from neophobic to neophilic, the 'haters' and 'lovers' of the new; it is this latter category which corresponds to the opportunists. The opportunist animal is playful and exploratory, and it is this which adds variation to behaviour. Thorpe (1964) suggests that exploration is a drive independent of the homeostatic drives and both Chance and Mead (1955) and Shillito (1963) have noted that exploratory behaviour occurs when an animal is confronted by a new environment and also from time to time in familiar surroundings. Indeed, Russell and Russell (1961) suggest that exploration is an important component of intelligence. Morris (1964), with his considerable experience of observing animals in captivity, has shown how opportunists contrive to introduce novelty into the most sterile environments: by forcing human beings to react to them, by manipulating objects or by more stereotyped activities such as continuously walking backwards and forwards in their confined quarters.

Morris stresses endogenous motivation or what he calls 'independent neo-philic motivation'.

Butler however, in his research on the investigatory behaviour of primates, suggests external stimuli as evoking the drive. In one experiment, Butler describes how a rhesus monkey had to discriminate between a door that would not open and one that opened onto a view of other animals, bowls of fruit, or moving inanimate objects:

> 'Three monkeys were put to the door-opening test hour after hour, with thirty seconds between trials, until they quit. One monkey performed for nine continuous hours!' (1954, p.6).

Butler concludes that food was less of an incentive than the sight of conspecifics but one might add, following Morris, that in the sterile laboratory environment the opening and shutting of a door is a reward in its own right.

Clearly there must be survival value for exploratory behaviour to have been selected: it gives the maximum exposure to the environment which allows for exploitation by non-specialist animals. Omnivorous 'opportunists' need a wide variety of responses if they are to exploit their surroundings successfully. Its origins must be sought in those less rigid aspects of instinctive behaviour — the 'appetitive' search behaviours which occur prior to a rigid sequence of behaviours. A novel stimulus, however, is potentially dangerous and time spent investigating implies a corresponding loss of vigilance and as Russell and Pearce note:

> 'a high level of predator danger would not favour a high level of investigatory activity' (1971, p.320).

Protoculture

Exploratory behaviour and the linking together of previously untried sequences of behaviour is characteristic of many primates, and in their case appears to have given rise to the establishment of proto-cultures. The concept of culture is one which sociologists would prefer to associate with only one species — *Homo sapiens.* The observations in recent years by many ethologists now makes this a difficult position to substantiate. Japanese scientists, in particular, have observed how new food preferences, food washing techniques and other behavioural adaptations are discovered by exploratory animals and passed on to other members of a group, until they become part of the repertoire of the group. One group of Japanese monkeys was provided with wheat which was thrown onto a sandy beach. The grains of wheat became contaminated with the sand making the eating of the food difficult. One exploratory individual threw handfuls of the contaminated grain into the sea — this may have been playful or accidental but she noted that the grain floated whilst the sand sank. She incorporated this behaviour into her repertoire and was soon copied by other young monkeys. Older females and finally the dominant adult males later followed their example and it now forms part of the behavioural repertoire of the group (see for instance Altmann, 1965). The Japanese observations are interesting. It is usually the youngest most exploratory members of the group who 'discover' the new behaviour; it is passed on to their peers, their mothers and finally to the more conservative dominant males. Indeed, a number of new behaviours have been stopped from spreading through a group by the intervention of dominant animals.

Proto-cultures are also a marked feature of chimpanzee groups. Thus one ethologist Sabater Pi, sounding more like an archaeologist, has given the following description of 'elementary industries' among chimpanzees in West Africa:—

> 'There exists unquestionable purposefulness in the manufacture of these sticks. They have a determinate diameter, their type is relatively uniform, and we believe they are adequate for the purpose for which they are designed, which is to perforate the earth to dig holes . . .' (1974, p.382).

Exploratory behaviour, learning and the establishment of proto-cultures to some extent emancipate animal species from the fixed action patterns discussed earlier and allow for the more flexible exploitation of resources. However, once established a learnt response can be as inflexible as inbuilt behaviour patterns: this is as true of the human animal as of the non-human as DeBono has forcefully demonstrated in his lateral thinking experiments (1973, 1976). It is here that a new mechanism, intelligence, begins to play an important role.

In his analysis of intelligence, Halstead (1947) isolates a number of factors, one of which he calls the 'P' factor. Halstead describes the dynamic relationship between affect and cognition and asks how reason gains ascendancy over affective demands:

> 'Must we not seek out a third factor which serves to buffer these affect demands in the face of the psychologically 'new', holding them in abeyance until the A factor can make its penetration into the entropy of unstructured time and space? For most certainly it will prove to be a factor which has strengthened from species to species, until it now underlies man's superior capacity for ego growth' (1947, p.70).

If intelligence was to evolve out of older instinctual systems, an inhibitory mechanism had to develop: the original link between releaser and action pattern had to be broken. Stenhouse interprets the P factor as procrastination or the 'postponement of action' (1974). Halstead does not elaborate on his hint that intelligence is an evolved phenomenon, but if we are to understand the evolution of the P factor we must look for it in species in which the chances of immediate flight or fight are reduced, and where immediate sexual gratification or desire for food has to be controlled by the individual. The primates are ideal candidates: their dependence on vision favours advanced warning, and as I will now explain, their social organisation favours procrastination.

Primate Social Behaviours

Primates often live in complex social groupings; however, sociality can create problems, particularly for subdominant animals: to succeed in a primate group they have to be able to postpone reaction. Michael Chance, for instance, has shown that there is inherent conflict in the position of subdominant adult males (1963). Living as they do in permanent bi-sexual groupings, in which there are usually some receptive females, the subordinate males are subject to continuous 'mating provocation': they are presented with sexual stimuli, both visual and olfactory, communicated by oestrous females, but simultaneously they are confronted by the presence of more dominant males. There is therefore a balance of negative and positive stimuli which forces the subordinate to procrastinate. One answer, which does occur occasionally, is for young adult males to leave the group, but the nature of the primate bond is to remain within the protection of the group. The dominant animal may be a potential threat but he is also a source of protection. Fox (1975), closely following Chance's argument, has suggested that a form of social selection has taken place favouring controlled and skilful animals:

> 'The more the emotions of aggression and lust come under cortical control the better the chance the animal had of surviving and passing on his genes to the next generation' (1975, p.48).

Sexuality and aggression, however, are only two aspects of the dilemma facing the subdominant animal; it is constantly having to modulate behaviour with reference to dominant animals — whether it wants food, a preferred sleeping site or a grooming partner; at the same time the animal must not move too far from the protection of the dominant. Chance (1976), has called this 'equilibration'.

A successful primate therefore is a controlled animal assessing the social context in which it finds itself, and experiments by Delgado back up the behavioural data. Delgado (1969) implanted electrodes into the brains of monkeys which, when stimulated, produced aggressive behaviour, but this behaviour was dependent on the animal's position in the social hierarchy; thus a dominant animal would show aggression whereas a low ranking animal would not. However, if the same low ranking animal was put into another group where it had a higher status it would exhibit aggression when the electrical stimulation of the brain took place.

There is more to the problem of social living than mere control: when blocked from a desired resource, a primate will attempt to solve its problems by what may be termed 'social tool using'. It is well known that primates are adept manipulators. Structurally, they have evolved hands which allow for the careful manipulation of objects (Le Gros Clarke, 1965), and Köhler's classic experiments suggest that intelligent tool use is a feature of chimpanzees. In a typical experiment, a chimpanzee would be put in a cage and food placed outside, beyond its reach. A stick (or two short sticks which could be fitted together) would be placed behind the animal in the cage. For a successful solution, the animal had to move away from the objective (i.e. control immediate response), put the two sticks together, return to the bars of the cage, orientate the composite 'tool', and sweep in the reward. An insightful solution, as far as Köhler was concerned, occurred when there was a 'single continuous occurrence, a unity as it were . . .' (1957, p.21).

The main criticism of Köhler's work is that he was apparently unaware that chimpanzees spontaneously use sticks and other objects, behaviour which seems to be part of the innate repertoire of the species (Chance 1967). Schiller (1967), Bolwig (1963) and others suggest therefore that insight was not involved. Parker (1980) however, suggests that the quantity and quality of manipulation does at least predispose the animal towards the successful solution of such problems. Observations by Menzel (1972) do lend support to Köhler; he observed the spontaneous behaviour of nine captive chimpanzees over a six year period; gradually he saw emerge the spontaneous use of poles and branches as ladders which were ultimately used by the animals in an insightful manner. The development of the behaviour may be summarised briefly in a number of stages, but crucial changes occurred suddenly, very much as described by Köhler:

Stage 1. Infant chimpanzees climb vertical objects. Sticks are manipulated: *the innate behavioural repertoire.*

Stage 2. After several months the animals developed the habit of standing a branch upright and rapidly climbing up it before it fell down. The activity was perfected, imitated and incorporated into group play. There was no extrinsic motivation; *a self-rewarding activity.*

Stage 3. Four years later the pole climbing was utilized to look into Menzel's observation tower.

Stage 4. One week later the pole was propped up against the observation tower as a ladder.

Stage 5. The final stage is the most interesting. Some of the favourite trees in the compound had an electric fence around them to stop the animals climbing into them. Nearby, climbing frames were provided. Two weeks after Stage 4, the animals were back in the trees — the base of the 'ladder' had been placed on the narrow runway of the climbing frame and positioned so that its top was against the tree, thus circumnavigating the obstacle. Once more the manoeuvre was perfected; remarkably, one animal would place the base of the ladder, the other orientating the top.

(As a postcript the animals were now able to escape from the enclosure!).

There is evidence from the wild to confirm the use of sticks to solve problems. However, one is struck by the fact that man, a species which has specialised in technology, has evolved from an order of animals which is technologically naive (even with chimpanzees, tool-using is relatively uncommon). This brings me back to my comment on social tool-using. Much of the behaviour of a baboon or macaque is highly stereotyped but a number of behaviours occur regularly enough to allow the observer to suspect that elements are entering the repertoire which are freed from hormonal mechanisms and are subject rather to neo-cortical control.

In a group of rhesus monkeys studied by my wife and myself (1969, 1971, 1976) we often saw six month old animals dominating adult males and females. When food was thrown between the offspring of a high ranking female and an adult, the latter would initially start eating. The young animal would control its response, dash back to its mother, start screeching, dash towards the food, back to mother — screeching in the direction of the adult with the food. It would continue this activity until it had enlisted the support of the mother in the dominance interaction and it had obtained the food. This has all the appearance of a ploy in which other animals are being used in a complex social interaction. There are many such examples in macaque society, for example:—

(1) a female will present her backside to a dominant animal (submission) whilst threatening a rival, in what appears to be an attempt to enlist support.

(2) In some groups of Japanese macaques, young adult males who would normally move to the periphery of the group gain entry to the central core of dominant animals by playing with the offspring of high ranking females.

Whether at the baboon-macaque level it is justifiable to call these social ploys intelligent social tool-using is debateable; an interesting series of observations on the chimpanzee by de Waal (1982), however, suggests that the chimpanzee has a highly sophisticated ability to use such ploys. For instance, the level of affect control chimpanzees are capable of is suggested by the following:—

(1) Young adult males have to be furtive when mating (see my previous discussion of 'mating provocation'). Whilst watching an oestrous female, one young male had an erection (legs outstretched and penis erect is a sexual signal); on seeing the approach of a dominant male, he dropped his hand over his penis concealing it from the dominant's view.

(2) During a dominance display in which two males were vying for the dominant position in the group, both exhibited signs of emotional conflict. One of the males exhibited a fear grimace which he hid from the other until he had moved away. On another occasion, a dominant animal bared its teeth in fear, but then put its hands to its lips and closed its mouth.

(3) Young females tend to utter high pitched screeches during copulation. This has obvious problems for the clandestine mating of subdominant males — it attracts the attention of the dominant male. At the beginning of her mating sessions, one female would screech loudly when copulating with both high and low ranking animals, but when more experienced she only screamed with high rankers; with the low rankers she still exhibited the associated facial expressions but stifled the scream.

As de Waal remarks:—

> 'the noiseless scream gives the impression of violent emotions which are only controlled with the greatest of effort' (1982, p.50).

Chimpanzee Politics

The most extraordinary aspect of de Waal's study is the social tool-using which was a feature of the colony and gave de Waal the title of his book: 'Chimpanzee Politics'. His observations suggest that chimpanzees deliberately manipulate each other for social ends: they have evolved to the stage of intelligent, self-aware manipulators of social situations, a sort of primaeval version of C.P. Snow's 'Corridors of Power' or perhaps more aptly, Angus Wilson's 'Old Men at the Zoo'. He gives the example of two mothers sitting on either side of an older, more dominant female whilst their offspring play nearby. The infants start fighting. One of the mothers pokes the dominant female, points at the infants and the dominant female threatens both infants. De Waal's explanation is as follows:

> 'Conflicts between children regularly engender such tension between their mothers that they too come to blows. This tension is probably caused by the fact that each mother wishes to prevent the other from interfering in the children's quarrel . . . When the children's game turned to fighting, both mothers found themselves in a painful situation. Tepel (one of the mothers) solved the problem by activating a dominant third party . . .' (1982, p.47).

Ethologists, brought up in the tradition described earlier do not find it easy to use concepts usually reserved for the human species but this has been forced on them by the non-human primates. De Waal's analysis of the dominance struggles within the colony are particularly interesting. Between 1974 and 1976 a large adult male, Yeroen, was dominant.

However in the summer of 1976 he was dominated in his sleeping den by another male, Luit; when the rest of the colony was present Yeroen was supported by them in any dominance interaction. The first sign of challenge came when Luit openly mated with a female, and then later displayed in front of the dominant. Both males then embraced females. Later Luit attacked Yeroen but the latter was supported by most of the females. Luit had lost his first challenge. Gradually, by embracing or threatening, Luit was able to detach the females from Yeroen: in this he was supported by a third male, Nikkie. De Waal writes:

> 'The period of struggle for dominance between Luit and Yeroen was a tense but exciting one for us. It was a process full of twists and turns. For the first month it was not clear what the final outcome would be. Some days Yeroen seemed to be in control, bluffing Luit aside or chasing him away, assisted by the females . . .' (1982, p.106).

but the females became less willing to support him and on day 72, Yeroen was observed acting submissively to Luit. With this alteration in the dominance hierarchy, the third male, Nikkie, now tried to dominate Yeroen who used Luit: he would turn, grunting, to the new leader, nodding his head in the direction of Nikkie, and Luit would display in front of Nikkie. Soon, however, a new coalition developed between the beta and gamma males who would display in front of the dominant. Gradually the new ploy was to place Nikkie at the top of the dominance hierarchy.

I have described only a small part of what was a highly complex series of interactions which suggest the importance of control, the awareness of a wide network of social ties, and the ability to manipulate those relationships. It is tempting, indeed, given the fact that primates in the wild have seldom specialised in tool use, to look for the origins of intelligent problem solving in the social matrix rather than the 'technical' context (chimpanzee adroitness in social manipulation may also provide the background which allows them to learn the basics of 'language' in the laboratory situation). The efficiency of the control factor must not be overstated however. Observations by Köhler show how affect can override the P factor:

> 'A little stick is introduced into her cage; she scrapes the ground with it, pushes the banana skins together into a heap . . . Ten minutes later, fruit is placed outside the cage outside her reach. She grasps at it, vainly of course, and then begins the characteristic complaint of the chimpanzee; she thrusts both lips, especially, the lower, forward for a couple of inches, gazes imploringly at the observer, utters whimpering sounds, and finally flings herself on the ground on her back . . .' (1957, p.35).

During the 'political' struggles observed by de Waal, an unsuccessful dominance attempt would often be followed by an uncontrolled tantrum.

It should also be noted that a social environment which puts a premium on social tool using may stop the technical solution of a problem. This is typically the case in baboon/macaque groups in which most of an animal's attention is devoted to observing the behaviour of dominant animals (Chance's 'agonic' societies, 1976), but it also occurs in chimpanzee groups (Chance's 'hedonic' society) in which far less time is spent attending to dominants. Thus one of Menzel's subordinate chimpanzees, although successful in placing the tip of the ladder on the tree, failed to place the bottom on the runway because of the high level of arousal in the presence of a dominant animal. This should be of no surprise and once again it should be remembered that the brain is an evolved structure. Both Koestler (1976) and Sagan (1978) stress the importance of the work of Paul Maclean which suggests that the neo-cortex has been superimposed on older structures more typical of the lower mammals and reptiles. Koestler suggests that there is a lack of integration between the evolutionary ancient limbic system and the neo-cortex:

> 'To put it crudely: evolution has left a few screws loose somewhere between the neo-cortex and the hypothalamus' (1976, p.16).

There is obviously a vast difference between the instinctive behaviour of lower animals and the more flexible behaviour of the higher primates: genetic instructions have given way to extra-genetic learning strategies (although the predisposition to learn must have a genetic component). But intelligence presumes the capacity to unlearn, to be constantly recombining new experiences. Our nearest living relative, the chimpanzee, has this capacity. The origins of man's intelligent manipulation of his world would seem to lie deep in the social world of the primates.

It would be too complicated a task to continue the story here but with the emergence of a conceptualizing primate we begin to approach the level of extra-somatic information described by Karl Popper (1973) as *World-3,* and by de Chardin (1971) as the *noosphere,* in which models of the world are built up by an exploratory and categorizing primate, where knowledge grows by means of conjectures and refutations:

> 'Thus while animal knowledge and pre-scientific knowledge grow mainly through the elimination of those holding the unfit hypotheses, scientific criticism often makes our theories perish in our stead, eliminating our mistaken beliefs before such beliefs lead to our own elimination' (Popper 1973, p.261).

This would be, perhaps, too optimistic a conclusion; it puts too much emphasis on the power of intelligence and underestimates the evolutionary defects in the construction of the human brain: it should be tempered by my earlier comment that the P factor does not always control affect , and by Koestler's similar suggestion that groups of *Homo sapiens* have often been eliminated for false assumptions due to the evolutionary limitations put on human intelligence. Unlike H.G. Wells, however, I do not intend to look into the future and I conclude with an anonymous poem in 'Punch' magazine in 1893 which was a reply to the Wellsian forecast of 'Man in the Year Million'; the poem concludes:

> 'If the Pall Mall Gazette has thus been giving
> A forecast correct of this change immense,
> Our stars we may thank, then, that we shan't be living
> A million years from hence'.

Acknowledgements

My original interest in the evolution of intelligence developed during the conversations with Dr. M.R.A. Chance whilst I was an Honorary Research Associate at the Sub-department of Ethology, University of Birmingham. I must also acknowledge my debt to Dr. W.M.S. Russell and Dr. V. Reynolds for introducing me to the field of biosocial anthropology, and my co-worker on the research on rhesus monkeys, H.B. Waterhouse. Needless to say the views put forward in this paper are my own.

References

Altmann, S.A. (1965). *Japanese Monkeys.* Edmonton, Canada: University of Alberta.
Beach, F.A. (1961). The descent of instinct. In *Instinct,* edited by R. Birney and R. Teevan. New York: Van Nostrand.
Bolwig, N. (1963). Observations on the mental and manipulative abilities of a captive baboon. *Behaviour,* 22, 24-40.
Butler, R.A. (1954). Curiosity in monkeys. *Scientific American,* 190, 70-75.
Chance, M.R.A. (1963). The social bond of the primates. *Primates,* 4, 1-22.
Chance, M.R.A. (1967). Köhler's chimpanzees: how did they perform? In *Animal Problem Solving,* edited by A. Riopelle. Harmondsworth, Middlesex: Penguin Books.
Chance, M.R.A. and Larsen, R. (1976). *The Social Structure of Attention.* New York: John Wiley & Sons.
Chance, M.R.A. and Mead, A. (1955). Competition between feeding and investigation in the rat. *Behaviour,* 8, 174-182.
Clark, W. Le Gros (1965). *History of the Primates.* London: British Museum.
Darwin, C. (1881). *Formation of Vegetable Mould Through the Action of Worms.* Reprinted 1945. London: Faber & Faber.
Darwin, C. (1859). *The Origin of Species.* Reprinted 1962. London: Collier-Macmillan.
de Bono, E. (1973). *Po: Beyond Yes and No.* Harmondsworth, Middlesex: Penguin Books.
de Bono, E. (1976). *Practical Thinking.* Harmondsworth, Middlesex: Penguin Books.
de Chardin, T. (1971). *Man's Place in Nature.* London: Fontana (W. Collins).
Delgado, J. (1969). *Physical Control of the Mind.* New York: Harper & Row.
de Waal, F. (1982). *Chimpanzee Politics.* London: Jonathan Cape.
Fox, R. (1975). *Encounter with Anthropology.* Harmondsworth, Middlesex: Penguin Books.
Goodall, J. (1971). *In the Shadow of Man.* London: Collins.
Halstead, W.C. (1947). *Brain and Intelligence.* Chicago: University of Chicago Press.

Hoebel, E. (1960). The nature of culture. In *Man, Culture and Society,* edited by H. Schapiro. Oxford: Oxford University Press.

Huxley, J. (1914). *The Courtship Habits of the Great Crested Grebe.* London: Jonathan Cape

Koestler, A. (1969). *The Act of Creation.* London: Pan Books.

Koestler, A. (1976). *The Heel of Achilles.* London: Pan Books.

Köhler, W. (1957). *The Mentality of Apes.* Harmondsworth, Middlesex: Penguin Books.

Linden, E. (1976). *Apes, Men and Language.* Harmondsworth, Middlesex: Penguin Books.

Lorenz, K. (1967). *On Aggression.* Oxford: Oxford University Press.

Menzel, E. (1972). Spontaneous invention of ladders in a group of young chimpanzees. *Folia Primatologica,* 17, 87-106.

Menzel, E. (1973). Further observations on the use of ladders. *Folia Primatologica,* 19, 450-457.

Morris, D. (1964). *Patterns of Reproductive Behaviour.* London: Pan Books.

Oakley, K. (1956). *Man the Toolmaker.* London: British Museum.

Parker, C. (1980). Opportunism and the rise of intelligence. In *The Exercise of Intelligence,* edited by E. Sunderland and M. Smith. New York: Garland.

Popper, K. (1973). *Objective Knowledge: An Evolutionary Approach.* Oxford: Oxford University Press.

Russell, E. and Pearce, G. (1971). Exploration of novel objects by marsupials. *Behaviour,* 40, 312-322.

Russell, W.M.S. and Russell, C. (1961). *Human Behaviour.* London: Andre Deutsch.

Ryle, G. (1963). *The Concept of Mind.* Harmondsworth, Middlesex: Penguin Books.

Sabata, Pi. J. (1974). An elementary industry of the chimpanzees in the Okorobikó Mountains, Rio Muni (Republic of Equatorial Guinea), West Africa. *Primates,* 15, 351-364.

Sagan, C. (1978). *The Dragons of Eden.* London: Coronet (Hodder & Stoughton).

Schiller, P. (1967). Innate constituents of complex responses in primates. In *Animal Problem Solving,* edited by A. Riopelle. Harmondsworth, Middlesex. Penguin Books.

Shafton, A. (1976). *Conditions of Awareness.* Portland: Riverside Press.

Shillito, E. (1963). Exploratory behaviour in the short-tailed vole. *Behaviour,* 21, 145-154.

Stenhouse, D. (1974). *Evolution of Intelligence.* London: Allen & Unwin.

Tanner, N. (1981). *On Becoming Human.* Cambridge: Cambridge University Press.

Thorpe, W.H. (1964). *Learning and Instinct in Animals.* London: Metheun & Co.

Tinbergen, N. (1951). *The Study of Instinct.* Oxford: Oxford University Press.

Tinbergen, N. (1974). *Curious Naturalists.* Harmondsworth, Middlesex: Penguin Books.

Virgo, H. and Waterhouse, M. (1969). The emergence of attention structure amongst rhesus macaques. *Man,* 4, 85-93.

Waterhouse, M. and Waterhouse, H. (1971). Population density and stress in zoo monkeys. *The Ecologist,* 1, 19-21.

Waterhouse, M. and Waterhouse, H. (1976). The development of social organization in rhesus monkeys (Macacca mulatta) — an example of bimodal attention structure. In *The Social Structure of Attention,* edited by M.R.A. Chance and R. Larsen. London: John Wiley & Sons.

Wells, H.G. (1972). Man in the year one million. In *Apeman, Spacemen,* edited by L. Stover and H. Harrison. Harmondsworth, Middlesex: Penguin Books.

Sex-Differences on Piagetian Formal Operations Tasks: Where They Went and How to Find Them

MICHAEL SHAYER and JOHN WILLIAMS
Centre for Science and Mathematics Education, Chelsea College, London

The literature on sex differences on Piagetian tests of formal operations gives a confused picture. The purpose of this paper is to help show how the confusion arises and how it might be dispelled, by (1) highlighting some of the shortcomings of previous studies, (2) specifying basic requirements for systematic study in this field, and (3) presenting new data which go some way towards meeting these requirements.

Previous Investigations

Table I summarises some recent studies in which sex differences have been examined. Their shortcomings will be discussed in turn.

Sample size

With one exception the studies listed were carried out on small samples. Using samples of respectively 17, and (approximately) 4 subjects per year of age it was unlikely that Kuhn and Angelev (1976) or Kuhn, Langer, Kohlberg and Haan (1977) would have found significant sex differences. It may readily be calculated, using the table of the t-distribution, that if two samples have a mean difference of 0.4 standard deviations, each sample needs to be approximately 50 in size for the difference to be significant at the 5 per cent level. Similarly, samples need to be of the order of 200 to establish this level of significance if their means differ by 0.2 standard deviations. Since 0.2 to 0.4 is the range of many of the mean sex-differences quoted by Maccoby and Jacklin (1975) in their Tables 3.4 and 3.6 for tests of verbal and quantitative ability respectively, it can be seen that the existing Piagetian literature gives no support for the assertion that sex-differences are absent.

A related point is made by Plomin and Foch (1981): differences of this order are so small compared with the range of individual differences

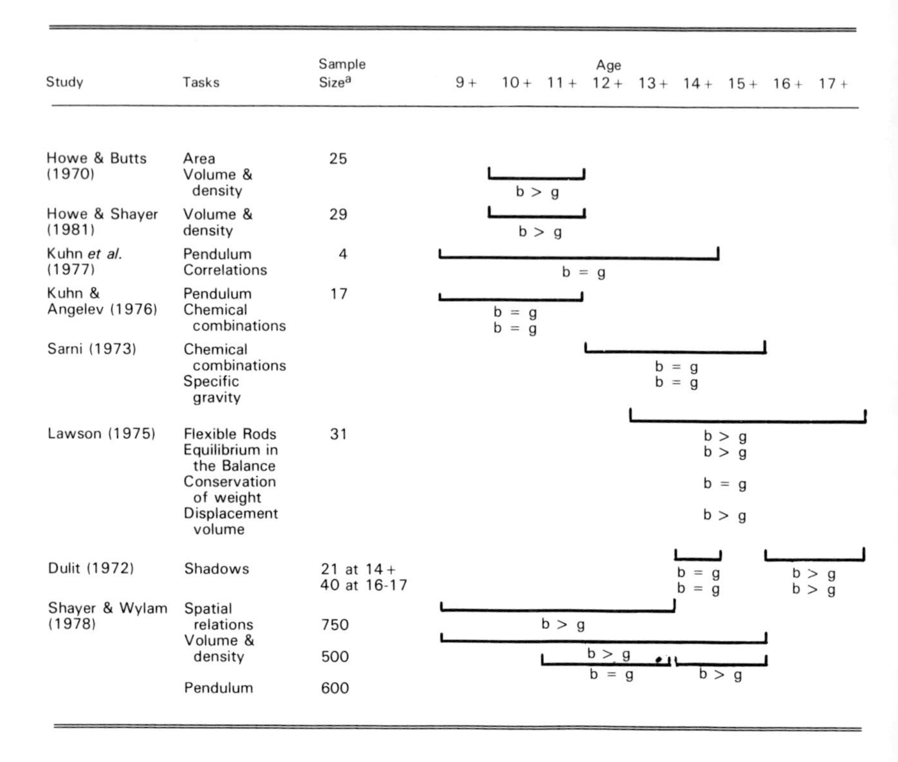

TABLE I

Studies of sex-differences and Piagetian tasks for different age-levels

Study	Tasks	Sample Size[a]	Age (9+ 10+ 11+ 12+ 13+ 14+ 15+ 16+ 17+)
Howe & Butts (1970)	Area Volume & density	25	10+ – 11+: b > g
Howe & Shayer (1981)	Volume & density	29	10+ – 11+: b > g
Kuhn *et al.* (1977)	Pendulum Correlations	4	9+ – 14+: b = g
Kuhn & Angelev (1976)	Pendulum Chemical combinations	17	9+ – 11+: b = g b = g
Sarni (1973)	Chemical combinations Specific gravity		12+ – 15+: b = g b = g
Lawson (1975)	Flexible Rods Equilibrium in the Balance Conservation of weight Displacement volume	31	13+ – 17+: b > g b > g b = g b > g
Dulit (1972)	Shadows	21 at 14+ 40 at 16-17	14+: b = g, b = g 16+ – 17+: b > g, b > g
Shayer & Wylam (1978)	Spatial relations Volume & density Pendulum	750 500 600	9+ – 13+: b > g 9+ – 15+: b > g 11+ – 13+: b = g; 14+ – 15+: b > g

Note: [a] Each number represents the number of girls in the Study: the number of boys was approximately the same.

within each sex that they are of little practical importance. While this is conceded in relation to the middle band of abilities, it will be shown below that such mean differences give rise to great differences where high level performances only are compared.

Sample ability: difficulty and discrimination

In testing subjects of representative ability on tasks of formal operations, a special problem arises out of the difficulty of these tasks which is likely to reduce their sensitivity in discriminating differences due to sex, task, or indeed any variable.

Table II gives, for some recent studies, the percentages of unselected children of about 14 years of age scoring at post-concrete and formal levels.

TABLE II

Percentages of unselected 14-year-olds attaining Early and Late Formal levels

	Sample size	3A	3B
Shayer et al. (1976)	1305	14.8	7.1
Lawson & Renner (1974)	108	19.0	3.0
Sayre & Ball (1975)	70		10.0

Used on subjects of this range the tests cannot be expected to discriminate well at the formal level. In normative studies there are good reasons for using samples which are representative of the normal range of ability in the population at large, but where sensitivity to special effects is needed on tests of this level of difficulty the case for using a high-ability sample is also strong.

Age as a relevant variable

Shayer and Wylam (1978), in a study to which we shall return later, found that sex differences vary with age. It is therefore unfortunate that the comparison groups of Kuhn, Langer, Kohlberg and Haan spanned five years (Table I), and even the comparison groups of Lawson (spanning four years) and Sarni (spanning three years) could be expected to blur the facts — especially as the sample age ranges of the latter two studies encompass the period 14-15 years — during which Shayer and Wylam found that important differences were likely to become established.

Task as a relevant variable

Lawson's and Shayer and Wylam's studies both suggest that the sex factor interacts with task factors. Among them, the studies in Table I cover a reasonable range of tasks, but unfortunately, task is badly confounded with age, for different tests are used at different ages.

Specification of test-procedure and performance criteria

A further obstacle to the comparison of results across studies arises from variation in test conditions from one study to another: (a) tasks are usually given in clinical interview form — with all the difficulties for specifying conditions which that implies; (b) criteria of assessment vary from study to study on the same task, and may be more lenient on one task than another. Moreover the assignments of specific test performances to stage-level not only differ from study to study, but were clearly in need of validation in their original publication (Inhelder and Piaget, 1958). Only in the case of *Pendulum* (Somerville, 1974) and *Chemical Combinations* (Dale, 1970) was the Genevan work replicated on a sufficient sample by interview so that Piaget's assignments could be cross-checked on the same subjects.

Specifically, Rowell and Hoffman (1975), Kuhn and Angelev (1976) and Kuhn *et al.* (1977) all use performance criteria for level 3B responses on the *Pendulum* task which are considerably more lenient than those used by Somerville (1974), Martorano (1977) and Shayer(1978). Such differences make it impossible to compare one sample with another or, on the same sample, one task with another. Where there is no agreement on test procedure and performance criteria there is little hope of obtaining a body of research in which individual studies contribute to one another's weight and precision.

How to Systematise Work in This Field

Where each subject must be individually tested, it is clearly a tall order to ask for the large samples required for the comparison of many tasks over many age levels. It was to permit Piagetian studies of reasonable size and complexity that the CSMS Science Reasoning Tests (National Foundation for Educational Research, 1979) were devised. These enable a whole school class to be tested in the time formerly taken for two individual pupils.

Moreover, each of the Science Reasoning Tests (SRTs) consists of a number (ranging from 13 to 21) of separately scored items — permitting the application of the normal spectrum of data-analysis procedures. The items can be grouped to yield scores corresponding to each of the Genevan behavioural descriptions of schemata quoted for a particular task. This permits comparison of performance on schemata both within and between tasks.

Thus a battery of tests has been developed which is self-consistent and consistent with the Piagetian assumption of a common conceptual infrastructure. This battery is making it possible to extend, to a wider range of tasks, the critical replication initiated by Somervill (1974) and Dale (1970) and to mount an integrated set of studies of formal operational thinking which support and qualify one another (Shayer, 1978; 1979), among which are those reported in this article.

TABLE III

Sex-differences related to age on Volume and Heaviness task

Mean age	Sample size		Mean levels[b]		Size of mean difference[a]	Standard deviation		t value of mean difference and (W^2)[c]
	Boys	Girls	Boys	Girls		Boys	Girls	
10/0	253	314	3.24	2.84	0.36	1.173	1.061	4.26(0.02)
11/1	545	454	3.49	3.30	0.16	1.255	1.062	2.55(0.01)
12/1	873	852	4.17	3.63	0.43	1.280	1.260	8.83(0.04)
13/1	981	798	4.38	3.83	0.46	1.181	1.209	9.67(0.05)
14/1	689	501	4.66	4.42	0.23	1.089	1.097	3.74(0.01)
15/6	434	399	4.85	4.39	0.42	1.040	1.102	6.20(0.04)

Note:

The scoring of the *Volume and Heaviness* task is on an equal interval scale from pre-operational = 1 through late concrete, 2B, = 4 to early formal, 3A = 6.

[a] Mean difference is the difference between means divided by the root mean square SD. All the differences are significant below the 0.001 level with the exception of that for age 11 ($p < 0.02$).

[b] All the yearly increments are significant beyond the 1 per cent level except that for girls between 14/1 and 15/6, which is a non-significant loss.

[c] W^2 as the proportion of total variance accounted for by sex-difference, is included following the recommendation of Hyde (1981).

Report of Findings from Two Studies

Two separate bodies of data will be analysed, the first giving performance at different ages on one task involving verbal reasoning and another involving spatial relationships, and the second comparing the performance of 14 year olds on five formal tasks.

Study (a): a sex-differential relating to age

Discussion. Shayer and Wylam (1978), in a study of sex differences, found boys and girls equal on the *Pendulum* task but boys superior on

Volume and Heaviness between the ages of 11+ and 14+, and that both boys and girls improved on both tasks during this period. *Volume and Heaviness* is a composite SRT ranging from the early concrete (2A) to early formal (3A) stages, and incorporating conservation of mass, weight, internal volume, displacement volume, intuitive density and density as a mass/volume relationship. This sex-differential can plausibly be related to those studies reported in Maccoby and Jacklin where girls are consistently at a disadvantage on tests involving spatial relationships. Here the data reported previously are analysed further to reveal the variation with age.

An age-sex interaction. Table III is derived from the tables of percentages given in Shayer and Wylam (1978).

It can be seen that there are two ages at which girls, despite their inherent disadvantage, approach the performance of boys: at 11 and 14 years of age. Perhaps the fact that girls tend to catch up at the age of

TABLE IV

Sex-differences related to age on the Pendulum task

Mean age	Sample size		Mean levels[a]		Size of mean difference	Standard deviation		*t* value of mean difference
	Boys	Girls	Boys	Girls		Boys	Girls	
12/3	549	597	2.29	2.37	−0.08	1.110	1.117	−1.29 (*n.s.*)
13/4	874	683	2.39	2.39	0	1.205	1.215	0
14/4	580	517	2.50	2.62	−0.10	1.207	1.206	−1.63
15/6	651	539	2.99	2.86	+0.11	1.241	1.133	+1.93 ($p<0.05$)

Note:

Scoring of the *Pendulum* task is on an equal interval scale from $2B^{-}$ = 1; late concrete, 2B = 2; 2B/3A = 3; 3A = 4, to late formal, 3B = 5. Add 2 to the mean values to compare with Table III.

[a] The yearly increment for girls between 12/3 and 13/4 is non-significant; the increments for boys between 12/3 and 13/4 and between 13/4 and 14/4 are significant at the 5 per cent level, and the increments for boys between 14/4 and 15/6 and for girls between 13/4 and 14/4 and between 14/4 and 15/6 are all significant below the 0.05 per cent level.

14 can be explained by their general adolescent growth spurt, which takes place on average just before that age, but which occurs about a year and a half later in boys. No such explanation is available for the approach to parity at the age of 11, and discussion of this is deferred until the summary section. Table IV gives the corresponding information for the formal *Pendulum* task.

Like Table III, Table IV shows that girls are at least level with boys at 14 years of age. Although the 11+ group is not included in Table IV, the girls are shown to be ahead of the boys at 12+. But before the fine detail of this comparison is examined, a very important sex-difference is shown in Table V, a difference which was obscured by the comparison of mean differences.

It can be seen that between the ages of 14 and 15½ an extra 7 per cent or more differential opens up between boys and girls in formal performance on both tasks. On *Volume and Heaviness* this means a drop in the relative proportion of girls to boys showing early formal thinking

TABLE V

Sex differences in Formal thinking on the Pendulum and Volume & Heaviness tasks

	Volume and Heaviness per cent 3A and above		Pendulum per cent 3A and above		Pendulum per cent 3B and above	
Mean Age	Boys	Girls	Boys	Girls	Boys	Girls
10+	1.9	–	–	–	–	–
11+	5.8	4.3	–	–	–	–
12+	15.2	8.1	15.0	16.4	3.3	2.7
13+	18.3	9.6	19.9	20.8	5.7	5.7
14+	24.9	18.5	22.6	25.0	7.7	8.6
15/6	31.1	16.9	34.4	27.2	16.3	9.0

Note: *n* as in Tables III and IV.

from about three quarters to about a half. Yet in Table III the relative mean change on the whole sample on this test is only 0.19 (0.42-0.23) standard deviations. Relatively small changes in the mean of a distribution can generate quite large differences in the numbers above a given high cut off point. The relationship is in fact an exponential one, and is used routinely in the quantitative handling of reaction kinetics in the physical sciences. This is conveniently demonstrated for psychologists by Hyde (1981) in her Figures 1 and 2 on page 899.

It can therefore be seen that the magnitude of the mean differences shown both here and in Maccoby and Jacklin's tables can have very substantial consequences where high level performance is concerned. The difference opened up between boy and girl populations between the ages of 14 and 15/6 is striking, and, if the ability to utilise formal thinking is important in adult life, this difference is of great consequence. Table V shows that although boys show their greatest relative increase in mature formal thinking (3B) between ages of 14 and 15/6, girls show no increase in the proportion utilising formal thinking (3A or 3B) after 14/4 on either Piagetian measure (the change from 25 to 27.2 per cent at $3A^+$ on *Pendulum* has a t value of only 0.85).

The meaning of this differential depends on the argument that the *Pendulum* task in no way discriminates boys from girls. In studies where this task has been used on children of 14 years of age or below, boys never show superior formal performance. Moreover (see also study (b)), boys show no significant differences in performance between this and other formal tasks, and there is no significant difference between the girls' performance at 14 years on *Pendulum* and the boys' performance on *Pendulum* and all the other formal tasks. Thus the differential which opens up on both tasks between boys and girls between the ages of 14 and 15/6 cannot be attributed to the nature of the task, since it occurs on the *Pendulum* task also. Here there is a true life-span differential. In the light of this evidence, earlier Piagetian studies which have reported sex-differentials in formal thinking in favour of males will need re-examining to see whether the differential can be attributed to the nature of the task or to the ages of the subjects.

In Figures 1(a) to (d) the annual percentage increments on both tasks are represented for boys and girls for the development of at least mature concrete and formal operational thinking respectively. In Shayer and Wylam (1978) it was further shown, by analysis of the boys' results on *Pendulum* broken down into three-month age intervals between the ages of 15/0 and 16/0 that there was no significant increase in the percentage of boys using formal operational thinking over this age-range. The cessation of development in the girls' population by the age of 14 is paralleled by a similar cessation in the boys' early in their fifteens. Thus in Figure 1 there is a final developmental spurt to be noted in each

FIGURE 1 Annual increments (as percentages) in the proportion of children using different levels of thinking at different ages

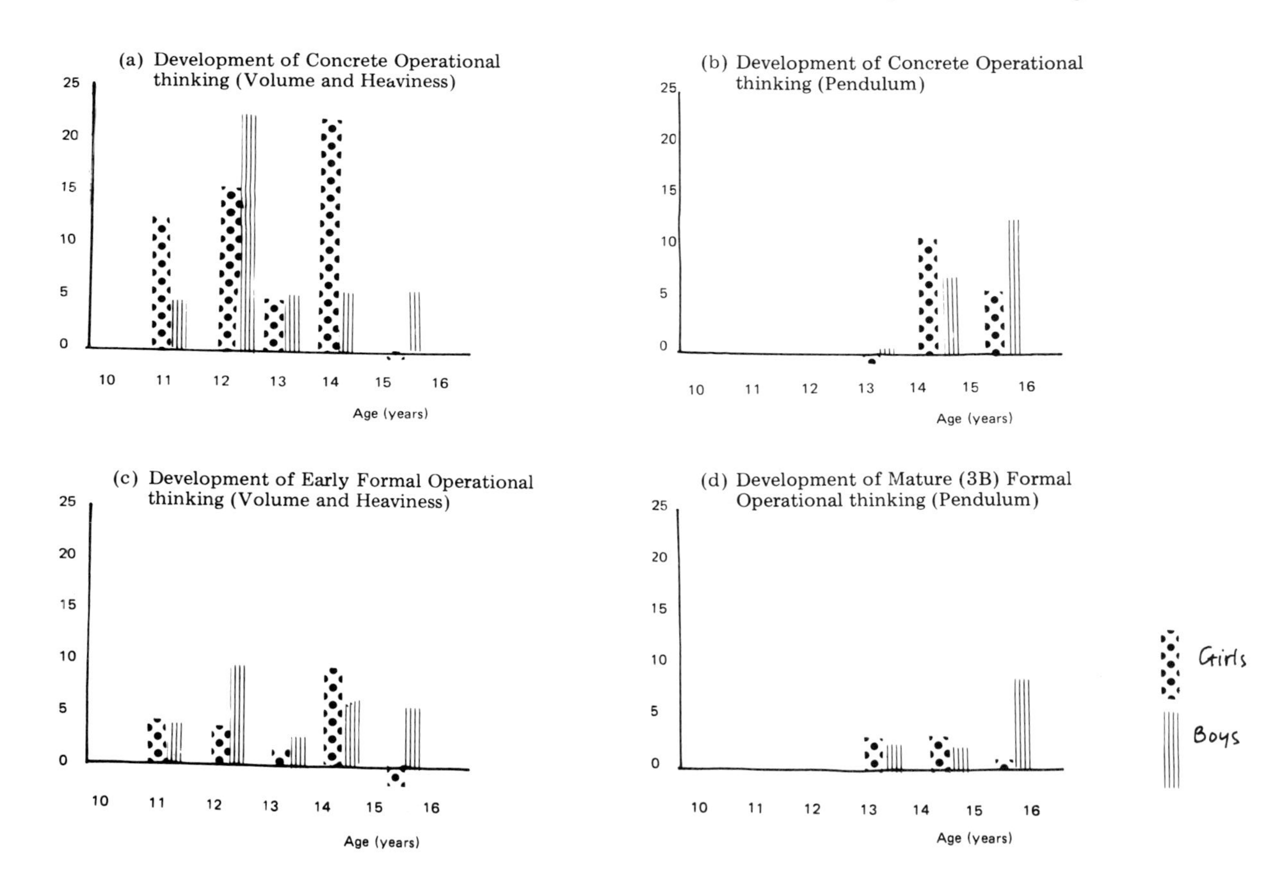

diagram which may plausibly be attributed to their asynchronic adolescent growth spurt.

However, there are further periodicities to be observed in Figure 1 which cannot be explained in this way. Both for boys and girls there is a relative plateau of development between the ages of 12 and 13, and likewise a very marked cognitive developmental growth spurt occuring between the ages of 10 and 12. The girls seem to lead the boys by about six months during this phase. Evidence may be cited both from Lovell and Shields (1967) and Webb (1974) that no matter how far up the ability range the sample is drawn (in the latter paper the criterion was WISC IQs of at least 160) formal operational thinking is not observed in children before the age of ten. One is therefore presented with two questions: What physiological and/or sociological causation can be adduced for Lovell and Webb's data, and why is the development of formal operational thinking not universal in adolescents? It appears to the authors that although plausible sociological explanations can be suggested for *either* of these two questions, contradictions must appear when the attempt is made to apply them to *both.* If the socialisation of late primary and early secondary schooling is the cause, then why the plateau between 12 and 13? If life-style differences and environmental expectations account for the non-universal development of formal operational thinking, why the periodicities? Further discussion of this point will be deferred until the summary: here it will only be suggested that it appears to the author that only some brain-physiological cause quite separate from adolescent development appears to promise to account for the present data without contradicting that of Lovell and Webb.

Study (b): sex-task interactions on five formal tasks

This study compares boys and girls on five tests of formal operations (*Pendulum, Equilibrium in the Balance, Inclined Plane, Chemical Combinations* and *Flexible Rods*) at the average age of about 14/3 — that is, just before their performance begins to diverge due to the continued development of the boys. This gives interesting sex-task interactions which are not confounded with this later divergence in performance. The findings reported here have not been published previously, but the same data-base was used to investigate the unity of formal operational thinking (Shayer 1978; 1979).

Sample. As shown in Table IV, Shayer and Wylam (1978) had found no significant difference between boys and girls on the *Pendulum* task for 14 year olds. In the sample of 600 14 year olds studied in Shayer (1979) there was a sub-sample of approximately 100 boys and 100 girls who were being taught in the same two comprehensive schools (mixed). Their scores on the *Pendulum* task were, Boys m = 3.005, sd 1.114, girls, *m* = 3.021, *sd* 1.066. Here, too, boys and girls showed identical performance. For this reason *Pendulum* was used as the matching variable for the two comparison groups. The groups are contributed by classes drawn from four schools as shown in Table VI.

TABLE VI

Source of study (b) sample — school x class x sex

			boys	*girls*
School 1:	selective-school boys	1 class	31	–
School 2:	selective-school boys	2 classes	57	–
School 3:	selective-school girls	4 classes	–	87
School 4:	non-selective mixed	3 of 4 top classes (from 9-class entry)	40	45
			128	132

It is reasonable to assume that both boys and girls in this sample represent the top 20 per cent of the population at large. The choice of subjects of this level of ability was informed by the results of Shayer, Küchemann and Wylam (1976) who, on a sample of 14-year-old children drawn from the top 20 per cent of the ability range obtained frequencies for the early formal (3A) and late formal (3B) level performance on the *Pendulum* problem of, respectively, 40.9 and 23.3 per cent. As pointed out earlier, tests of formal thinking can be expected to be much more sensitive to differences on a more able sample.

Method. Five Science Reasoning Tasks (standardised class tests — see section 2) were administered by the research team (all males) in the following fixed order *Pendulum, Equilibrium in the Balance, Inclined Plane, Chemical Combinations* and *Flexible Rods* over a four-month period.

Results. Table VII presents the results.

It can be seen from Table VII that only with the tasks *Equilibrium in the Balance* and *Inclined Plane* are there significant sex differences, and that these are even greater than was the case with *Volume and Heaviness.* In Table VIII *Pendulum* is compared with the four other tasks.

TABLE VII

Sex-differences on five formal tasks (14 year-olds)

Task	Sample size		Mean levels		Mean diff.	Standard deviation		t value of difference
	Boys	Girls	Boys	Girls		Boys	Girls	
Pendulum	128	132	3.56	3.54	0.02	1.11	1.03	0.15 (*n.s.*)
Equilibrium in the Balance	125	133	3.59	3.01	0.54	1.12	1.08	4.23 ($p<0.001$)
Inclined Plane	126	131	3.54	2.93	0.57	1.03	1.10	4.58 ($p<0.001$)
Chemical Combinations	129	120	3.57	3.57	0	0.94	0.95	0
Flexible Rods	130	133	3.67	3.54	0.13	0.98	1.04	1.04 (*n.s.*)

Note:

The scoring of the tasks is on an equal interval scale from $2B^{-}$ = 1, late concrete 2B = 2, 2B/3A = 3, 3A = 4, to late formal 3B = 5. Add 2 to the mean values to compare with Table III.

This is the evidence which justifies the assertion that boys show no significant differences on any of these formal tasks, and that girls perform on *Pendulum* at the same level as do boys on all formal tasks. These inter-task differences for girls agree well with those published by Martorano (1977) on a sample of 80 girls between the ages of 11 and 18. For the four tasks in common (*Inclined Plane* not used by Martorano) the relative means show the same pattern, after adjusting for the more selected sample range used in the present study.

Discussion

Two separately describable types of sex-differences in performance on Piagetian tasks have been reported. The first is a life-span developmental difference. Boys and girls aged fourteen and below can be expected to perform equally on Piagetian tests involving verbal and logical reasoning, particularly if the task-solution is counter-intuitional (*Pendulum, Chemical Combinations, Flexible Rods*). Any differences which exist favour girls. Yet between the ages of 14 and 15½ one can expect a higher proportion of boys to develop formal operational thinking on all Piagetian tasks, and for boys to increase their lead over girls on those tasks in which they were already at an advantage by 14. Any male

TABLE VIII

Comparison of Pendulum scores with scores on four formal tasks (14-year-olds)

Task	Boys		Girls	
	Mean differences	Significance of difference	Mean differences	Significance of difference
Equilibrium	+0.03	*n.s.*	−0.50	$p<0.001$ (t = 5.99)[a]
Inclined Plane	−0.02	*n.s.*	−0.55	$p<0.001$ (t = 6.75)
Chemical Combinations	+0.01	*n.s.*	+0.03	*n.s.*
Flexible Rods	+0.11	*n.s.* (t = 1.4)	0	*n.s.*

Note:
[a] t-values are higher than in Table VII because means are correlated.

population sampled at ages higher than 14 will therefore be show superior performance for this reason. As can be seen from Table V nearly twice as many boys (16 per cent compared with 9 per cent) as girls show the highest level of formal thinking by the age of 15½. It is suggested that males obtain a developmental advantage due to their later adolescent growth spurt.

Second, on certain tasks boys' performance is always superior. *Equilibrium in the Balance* and *Inclined Plane* have in common that their solution is likely to be helped by an intuitive non-verbal feeling for the true or likely relationship between the physical variables of force, length and weight, and compound variables such as work. Such intuition will depend upon good spatial abilities as well as reasoning ability. *Volume and Heaviness* is different from the purely formal tests in that only a few items depend on the subject showing a solution strategy at the time of the test. Most of the conservation items depend upon the interpretation which the subject has already put upon reality. But the physical conservations depend also upon the interaction between experience and spatial abilities and one may need to look no further than the sex-difference on spatial tests to account for these Piagetian tasks where the female is always at a relative disadvantage.

In addition, a developmental singularity common to both boys and girls has been reported. There is a developmental spurt on both concrete and formal operational measures occuring between the ages of 10 and 12, in which girls lead boys by about six months, followed by a relative plateau of development between the ages of 12 and 13. It has already been argued that this spurt is prior to adolescence both for boys and girls, and that some common brain-growth phenomenon is the most plausible candidate as an explanatory model. Epstein (1980) has cited several sources of evidence for a periodicity of brain development, with a growth spurt between the ages of 10 and 12, followed by a plateau, and has also argued on general mammalian growth principles that it is unlikely that an organism would evolve to timetable *two* major growth phenomena simultaneously (brain-growth and adolescent growth). John (1977) has assembled data which show that the proportion of total brain rhythm energy in the alpha frequency bands during a state of relaxation is correlated with psychometric measures, and has presented yearly cross-sectional data on the growth of this proportion. The difference between his quoted 8, 9, 10 and 11 plateau and his 12 to 14 plateau is over four standard errors, and of magnitude 0.6 standard deviations on his sample ranges. It is claimed merely that the most parsimonious explanation available of the Piagetian data referred to in the present paragraph is that they are an aspect of qualitative and possibly quantitative changes in the brain which seem to be 'timetabled' to permit a further change in cognitive complexity (formal operational thinking) which the organism will need in adolescence. Clearly longitudinal evidence on samples receiving both Piagetian and brain-physiological measures would be required to establish this connection.

Lastly, it has been argued that much of the confusion in the literature on Piagetian tasks and gender-differences referred to by Neimark (1975) can be traced to a combination of inadequate samples and variable behavioural criteria used by workers in the field, rather than to the original Genevan research. Our own group-tests have utilised all the behavioural criteria of the Inhelder and Piaget research, and preserved the detail of developmental stage sub-levels originally used in assessment. This has made possible the research presented in this article. It is hoped that some contribution to clarity has been made.

Acknowledgments

The data for studies (a) and (b) were collected as part of the Social Science Research Council project, Concepts in Secondary Mathematics and Science (CSMS, 1974-1980), and analysed further as a contribution to the SSRC project, Cognitive Acceleration through Science Education (CASE, 1980-1983).

References

Dale, L.G. (1970). The growth of systematic thinking: replication and analysis of Piaget's first chemical experiment. *Australian Journal of Psychology,* 22, 277-286.

Dulit, E. (1972). Adolescent thinking à la Piaget: the formal stage. *Journal of Youth and Adolescence,* 1, 281-301.

Epstein, H. (1980). Correlated brain and intelligence development in humans. In *Development and Evolution of Brain Size,* edited by M.E. Hahne, C. Jensen and B. Dudek, New York: Academic Press. Chapter 6.

Howe, A. and Butts, D. (1970). The effect of instruction on the acquisition of conservation of volume. *Journal of Research in Science Teaching,* 7, 371-375.

Howe, A. and Shayer, M. (1981). Sex-related differences in response to instruction on a volume and density task. *Journal of Research in Science Teaching,* 18, 169-175.

Hyde, J.S. (1981). How large are cognitive differences? *American Psychologist,* 36, 892-901.

Inhelder, B. and Piaget, J. (1958). The Growth of Logical Thinking. London: Routledge & Kegan Paul.

John, E.R. (1977). *Neurometrics: Clinical Applications of Quantitative Electrophysiology.* New York: John Wiley.

Kuhn, D. and Angelev, J. (1976). An experimental study of the development of formal operational thought. *Child Development,* 47, 697-706.

Kuhn, D., Langer, J., Kohlberg, L. and Haan, N.S. (1977). The development of formal operations in logical and moral judgement. *Genetic Psychology Monographs,* 95, 97-188.

Lawson, A.E. (1975). Sex difference in concrete and formal reasoning ability by manipulative tasks and written tasks. *Science Education,* 59, 397-405.

Lawson, A.E. and Renner, J.W. (1974). A quantitative analysis of responses to Piagetian tasks and its implications for curriculum. *Science Education,* 58, 545-559.

Plomin, N. and Foch, T.T. (1981). Sex differences and individual differences. *Child Development,* 52, 383-385.

Rowell, J.A. and Hoffmann, P.J. (1975). Group tests for distinguishing formal from concrete thinkers. *Journal of Research in Science Teaching,* 12, 157-164.

Sarni, C.I. (1973). Piagetian operations and field independence as factors in children's problem-solving performance. *Child Development,* 44, 338-345.

Sayre, S. and Ball, D.W. (1975). Piagetian cognitive development and achievement in science. *Journal of Research in Science Teaching,* 12, 165-174.

Shayer, M. (1978). *A Test of the Validity of Piaget's Construct of Formal Operational Thinking.* Ph.D. University of London.

Shayer, M. (1979). Has Piaget's construct of formal operational thinking any utility? British Journal of Educational Psychology, 49, 265-276.

Shayer, M., Küchemann, D.E. and Wylam, H. (1976). The distribution of Piagetian stages of thinking in British middle and secondary school children. *British Journal of Educational Psychology,* 46, 164-173.

Shayer, M. and Wylam, H. (1978). The distribution of Piagetian stages of thinking in British middle and secondary school children II: 14-16 year olds and sex differentials. *British Journal of Educational Psychology,* 48, 62-70.

Somerville, S.C. (1974), S.C. (1974). The pendulum problem. *British Journal of Educational Psychology,* 44, 266-281.

Webb, R.A. (1974). Concrete and formal operations in very bright 6-11 year olds. *Human Development,* 17, 292-300.

The Galton Lecture 1983: Intelligence: New Wine in Old Bottles

H.J. EYSENCK

Institute of Psychiatry, University of London, London

Galton's views of eugenics are fundamentally based on three major axioms. The first of these is that intelligence is a scientifically meaningful concept which underlies all cognitive behaviour, such as learning, problem solving, etc. The postulation of such a concept does not rule out the existence of other abilities, but it does assign supremacy to what later on came to be called the general factor of intelligence. It is not suggested that intelligence has any real *existence,* in the sense that physical objects exist; like all scientific concepts, such as heat, gravitation or elecricity, intelligence cannot and should not be reified, and indeed Galton never made that mistake.

The second crucial requirement is that intelligence should be a measurable quantity; measurement is vital when we want to select people in any way for the possession of a given trait or ability. Galton made several suggestions as to the best way of carrying out such measurement, including his view that reaction times would be a good measure, but beyond indicating the desirability of using physiological and relatively elementary measures he did not, as Binet did after him, proceed to create usable scales of measurement.

The third vital ingredient is of course that intelligence should be largely heritable; clearly without such heritability eugenics could not function. The demonstration of heritability is obviously dependent on the existence and measurement of intelligence, as defined above; only measurable quantities can be investigated by means of the methodology of behavioural genetics.

For Galton, a fourth requirement would seem to have been the supreme social utility of high intelligence; he rested his case for the application of the methods of eugenics very largely on the social importance of intelligence, and the need to enhance the intellectual performance of a given group or nation. We might be less inclined nowadays to emphasize so much the claims of intelligence in this respect. Altruism, which has recently been shown to be strongly heritable, as sociobiologists have predicted, is possibly from the simple point of survival of mankind a more important candidate than intelligence (Rushton *et al,* in press). From the

point of view of human happiness, personality traits like extraversion (positively) and neuroticism (negatively) are much more important than intelligence (Eysenck and Eysenck, 1984); here again, genetic factors have been found very important for happiness, extraversion and neuroticism. It might even be argued that any dramatic increase or equalisation in intelligence might have adverse consequences. In spite of the advances of computers and robots, there are many low-level jobs not demanding much intelligence whose performance is vital for society. A nation made up entirely of Einsteins, Beethovens and Raphaels could not long endure! The point is not a crucial one, but the events of recent years have led many people to a realisation that unbridled intelligence, without suitable value systems and altruistic impulses, may not be as advantageous as was once thought.

However that may be, the first three requirements which Galton saw as essential for any eugenic programme have been the subject of much controversy in psychological circles over the past hundred years, and in looking at some recent findings, which have revolutionised the whole topic, it will be important to avoid a semantic pitfall which has had unfortunate effects on past controversies and discussions. The term 'intelligence' has been used with three different meanings, and unless discussants specify the particular meaning they have in mind, debate becomes pointless. We have first of all intelligence A, i.e. the biological basis for our ability to perform successfully various cognitive functions, such as learning, problem solving, etc. The physiological basis invoked is also responsible for genetic differences in intelligence between different people, according to Galton, whose work is concerned essentially with this intelligence A.

Intelligence B, on the other hand, is concerned with the everyday application of cognitive ability to the intellectual and practical problems facing a person in his everyday life. Intelligence B is of course based on intelligence A, but many other factors enter to make the relationship less than perfect. Education and other influences which determine a person's knowledge base present an obvious example of such external factors; culture, socioeconomic status, the availability of newspapers, magazines and books, and many other such factors play a crucial role in determining the transition for any given person from intelligence A to intelligence B.

Intelligence C is concerned with the measurement of intelligence; typically, IQ tests would fill this role. As Figure 1 shows, different types of intelligence tests are differentially related to intelligence A and intelligence B. Verbal tests are usually measures of crystallized ability (g_c) and are usually closer to intelligence B; non-verbal or culture-fair tests of fluid intelligence (g_f) are usually closer to intelligence A. Physiological measures of intelligence (g_p), about which we shall have to say a great deal more later on, are probably closest to intelligence A,

FIGURE 1

Relations between intelligence A, B and C, and different measures of intelligence.

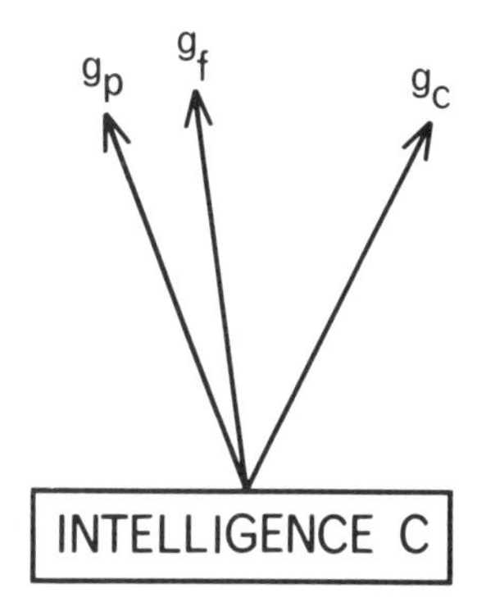

and possibly may be regarded as direct measures of it. Measures of reaction time may also be considered to fall into this group.

Galton's paradigm of intelligence as a general factor, genetically determined and constituting a biological disposition for cognitive functioning, and measurable by means of physiological investigations, was not universally accepted, and a rival paradigm, that of Binet, very largely carried the day. Where Galton was interested in intelligence A, Binet was interested in intelligence B; where Galton was interested in general intelligence, Binet was interested in a number of different abilities; where Galton was interested in genetics, Binet was interested in education. Binet in fact denied the scientific meaningfulness of intelligence, and preferred the notion of a large number of independent intellectual abilities, such as memory, suggestibility, verbal ability, etc.; 'intelligence' would then just be the relatively meaningless average of all these separate abilities. Thus the very existence of intelligence as a meaningful scientific concept was denied by Binet, and his many American successors. Typical of this approach is the recent work of Guilford (Guilford and Hoepfner, 1971), whose structure-of-intellect model of intelligence is shown in Figure 2. Guilford postulates five operations, having four different types of content, and producing six different types of products; the various combinations of these three classes produces 120 different and theoretically independent kinds of 'intelligence', for some 80 of which Guilford claims to have found some evidence. This breakdown of 'intelligence' into many 'intelligences' has in fact proved to be a *reductio ad absurdum;* as Eysenck (1979) has shown, the evidence is quite strong that these various types of tests are not in fact independent, but correlate highly with each other, and also with measures of general intelligence, such as the Wechsler test. Furthermore, factor analysis of intercorrelations between the tests shows a strong general factor, as well as a small number of independent abilities, such as verbal, numerical, visuo-spatial ability, very much as postulated by Thurstone (1938). The fit of Guilford's theory to the data is no better than chance.

FIGURE 2

Guilford's Structure-of-Intellect model of intelligence.

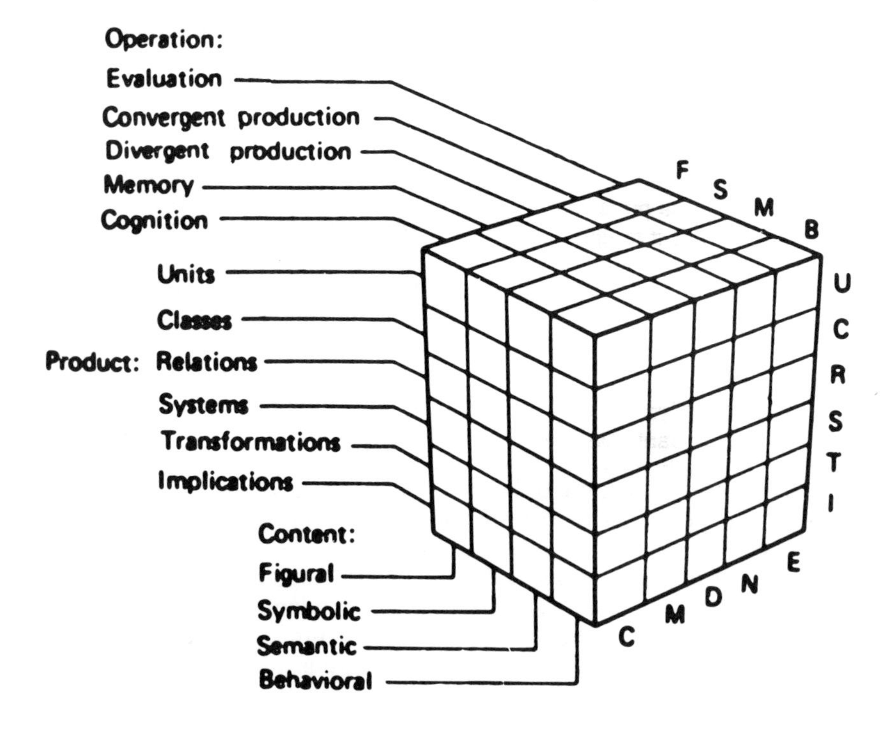

The psychometric evidence, therefore, is very much in favour of Galton's notion of a general factor of intelligence (*'g'*), with the important proviso that there are a number of special abilities, orthogonal to general intelligence, which contribute a small but not unimportant part to the variance of IQ tests, and to intelligence B in general. In addition, there is good evidence that personality variables also contribute to intelligence B; thus neuroticism was already found by Terman (Terman and Oden, 1959) in his well known study of 'genius', to be a very important factor in preventing the high IQ of some of his subjects from producing the expected intellectual and social success that was reached by others of similar IQ, but not burdened with emotional instability. From the point of view of intelligence B, therefore, and thus of life success, all these factors are very important, but we will here be concerned entirely with intelligence A, i.e. the general factor of intelligence as defined by Galton, Spearman, and Burt.

The success of Binet in constructing tests of intelligence of the familiar IQ type, i.e. tests which were largely geared to intelligence B, and which were obviously powerfully influenced by education, socioeconomic status, cultural factors etc., has led to never-ending arguments about the relative influence of nature and nurture, and has bedevilled the scientific investigation of many problems, ranging from sex differences and class differences in intelligence to the hypothetical deterioration of intelligence with age, and other equally important social questions. The fact that differences in IQ are powerfully determined by genetic factors, but that environmental factors also play a large part, has made the solution to these problems along experimental lines almost impossible, because even if it be agreed that only 20 per cent of the total variance on IQ tests is contributed by environmental factors, this is usually more than the observed differences between rich and poor, males and females, etc., thus leaving the field open to argument which, because of the unsatisfactory nature of the measuring instrument, cannot easily arrive at a solution independent of the assumptions made by different investigators (Eysenck, 1979).

The actual quantitative estimate of the contribution made by genetic factors to IQ differences is often said to be in doubt, but in actual fact there is fairly general agreement. Again the debate is clouded by semantic issues, such as a proper definition of 'heritability'. Geneticists may mean by this the 'narrow heritability', i.e. the contribution of additive genetic factors only. Or we may mean by it the 'broad heritability', which includes factors such as assortative mating, dominance and epistasis. Last, we may quote the heritability as calculated by traditional formulae, or we may make a correction to exclude the influence of measurement error, which is normally counted in as part of the environmental variance, but which should properly be excluded from consideration. We might thus estimate the heritability in a given study as being 50 per cent (narrow heritability, uncorrected), 60 per cent (broad heritability, uncorrected), or 70-80 per cent (broad heritability, corrected for attenuation). If different authors give different heritabilities, this may mean no more than that they have used different aspects of heritability; it does not imply factual differences of any kind.

We must also consider that heritability estimates are population statistics, i.e. they apply to a given population, at a given time, and there is no reason to assume that they will be identical from one population to another, or from one time to another. It is no criticism of a heritability study in England pre-war, which may have arrived at a figure of 80 per cent, to say that a more recent American study found a heritability of 50 per cent. There is no reason why the two should be identical, as the two cultures are different, and so are the times at which the investigations were done. It is reassuring to note that most studies which have been done in the United States, the United Kingdom, the Scandinavian countries, Germany, etc. come to pretty much the same general conclusions, ranging from 60-80 per cent of the variance (broad heritability, corrected), and recently similar studies have been reported from the Soviet Union, Poland and East Germany, suggesting that communist countries show as much variation in intelligence, and as much genetic causation of this variation, as do capitalist countries (Eysenck, 1982b). However, clearly the figures may change as social institutions change, and it should not be assumed that even at the present time the amount of variance accounted for by genetic factors in India, or China, or among the Eskimos would be identical with that observed in Europe, the USSR, or the USA.

In comparing the paradigms of Binet and of Galton, we may conclude that psychometric and genetic investigations have on the whole supported Galton's position. It is scientifically meaningful to postulate a general factor of intelligence, and this general factor is largely but not entirely produced by genetic causes. Yet the evidence is unsatisfactory, being entirely statistical in nature, and there are many criticisms to be made of the psychometric investigations of Binet-type tests. These investigations usually take total scores on a given test as the basic data; it is these scores that are then averaged, correlated, or subjected to factor analysis. Eysenck (1953) has always maintained that it is inadmissible to use total scores in this manner, because identical scores may be obtained along quite different lines. Thus John Doe, bright but impulsive and non-peristent, may get a given score because he succeeds with quite difficult problems, but makes many errors with relatively easy problems, and does not persist when he might have succeeded in solving the problem with more application. Mary Smith, who gets the same score, is much less quick in her thought processes, but persistent and given to checking her answers, so that although she only succeeds with easy and average-difficulty items, there are no errors in her work. Many other combinations of these various qualities are possible, and indeed found, and so are many different ways of putting together the same IQ score. Can it seriously be maintained that all these scores are in fact in any meaningful sense identical? Eysenck (1953) put forward the hypothesis that the IQ defined in terms of total scores of this kind, can in fact be broken down into three independent variables, namely mental speed, persistence, and error checking, and the important work of Furneaux (1960) and White (1982), who have contributed greatly to the development of this paradigm, has indeed shown that when we analyse success or failure on individual items, and the duration of time needed to solve correctly, solve incorrectly, or abandon each item, for each individual, three factors very much like those postulated above do emerge as independent contributors to the total IQ score. This is an important development in the theory of intelligence; we will not here discuss it at any length, but merely use it as a stepping stone to an entirely different kind of measurement which has come to the fore recently and which has threatened to overthrow completely the traditional way of measuring intelligence.

Binet's construction of IQ tests depended largely on the view that such tests should be of a relatively complex nature, involving learning, problem solving, and other activities based on high-level cognitive activities of various kinds. Such tests inevitably needed a knowledge base, and this led to the eternal disputes concerning the influence of nature and nurture on IQ differences. The knowledge base of one person would inevitably be different from that of another, and to the degree that the extent of the knowledge base influenced test performance, to that extent could it be said that the IQ was not a proper measure of intelligence.

Galton, on the other hand, favoured the physiological and simple sensory tests, and in their early work Spearman (1904) and Burt (1909) followed Galton's suggestions. Spearman used his newly found statistical methods to demonstrate 'the functional correspondence between intelligence and sensory discrimination', a result in good agreement with Galton's hypotheses.

Burt in his original study used a whole series of relatively simple tests involving among other tests what we would now consider examples of 'inspection time'; reference will be made again to this type of test. Other tests included simple motor reactions, sensory motor tests like card sorting, tests of immediate memory, etc., as well as more cognitive tests. It is interesting that his 'spot-pattern' test, i.e. the test of 'inspection time', had extremely high loadings on the general factor of intelligence. It is also interesting to note that in spite of these early successes of sensory, inspection and comparison tests neither Burt nor Spearman continued with these tests, but rather switched over to Binet-type tests.

As is well known, Spearman (1927) finally arrived at a theory of cognitive processes which he put in the form of his three 'noegenetic laws', i.e. the law of apprehension of experience, the law of eduction of relations, and the law of the eduction of correlates. If we take a simple number series test, such as the following 4, 5, 7, 10, 14, ?, we can see the role of apprehension of experience (we must apprehend the actual numbers given), followed by the eduction of relations (the difference between successive numbers always increases by one), and finally the eduction of correlates (applying the relation to the last number, the solution of the problem is 14 + 5 = 19). In this process Spearman assigned much greater weight to the eduction of relations and correlates, than to the apprehension of experience, even though his own early work and that of Burt suggested that this might not be the correct procedure.

The reason why reaction time measurement (and by implication other simple perceptual and motor tests) was rejected as a means of investigating intelligence, and hardly used at all for over 60 years, was the apparently negative outcome of a well-known investigation by Wissler (1901), who reported essentially zero correlations between reaction times and intelligence. This very influential study, however, was severely flawed. The measurement of reaction time was quite unsatisfactory, averaging for each person only three to five measurements, where at least a hundred would be required to obtain a stable average. Wissler did not use IQ tests at all, but relied for the measurement of intelligence on academic grades, which are not very reliable and not a good measure of intelligence. Last but not least, he used as the subjects selected students at a university, thus reducing the range of ability to such an extent that it is doubtful whether even a perfect measure of intelligence would have shown much correlation with the criterion. In spite of these obvious defects his results were taken seriously and influenced several generations of psychologists in their rejection of the Galtonian approach.

More recent work on reaction times has been summarised by Jensen (1982), and many interesting findings have been reported. In the first place, it was clear that even simple reaction times give highly significant correlations with IQ. Choice reaction times give even higher correlations, depending on the number of choices available, at least up to eight, corresponding to three bits of information; when choices get much more numerous than that, and reaction times go up to a second or so, there is no further increase in correlation with IQ, and indeed there may be a regression.

Of particular interest is the slope of the line defining the increase in reaction time with the increase in number of choices. This line follows Hick's Law, according to which there is a linear increase in reaction time with a logarithm to the base 2 of the number of choices offered, i.e. the bits of information involved. When there are two choices involved, we have one bit of information; when there are four choices, we have two bits; and with eight choices, we have three bits of information. Following Hick's Law, a straight line can be drawn through the average reaction times corresponding to these numbers of choices, and the slope varies with intelligence, high IQ persons having a much less steep slope than duller persons. In other words, the brighter a person is, the less does his reaction time increase with increase in the number of choices involved.

A third and last major finding was that IQ correlated negatively (and quite highly) with the *variability* of the reaction times recorded for a given subject. As pointed out above, reaction times are inherently variable, and to obtain a satisfactory average at least 100 must be measured and averaged. The variability of these 100 measurements is greater for dull people, and less for bright people; this correlation is in fact higher than that between IQ and reaction time itself, whether simple or choice. Taking all these measures together (simple reaction time, choice reaction time, slope and variability) and combining them into one score, we can obtain respectable correlations with IQ ranging from 0.6 to 0.8 depending on population samples and other similar factors.

Brand and Deary (1982) have discussed evidence to indicate that 'inspection time' and IQ are also quite highly correlated. A defining experiment here is one in which two lines, one clearly longer than the other, are presented in a tachistoscope to the subject for a short period of time, and he is required to indicate whether the right or left line is longer. Time of exposure is progressively reduced until he succeeds 97.5 per cent of the time; this constitutes his threshold. High IQ subjects have lower thresholds than low IQ subjects, not only for visual inspection times, but also for auditory ones, thus demonstrating the correctness of Burt's (1909) original results.

All these experiments indicate a much closer relationship between very simple sensory and motor reactions and IQ than the Binet-type approach, or Spearman's noegenetic laws, would have led one to anticipate, and it is perhaps not too strong a statement to say that these results are incompatible with the kind of view of the nature of intelligence that has been dominant in the last 80 years or so. The results are much more in line with Galton's theories, and powerfully suggest a re-evaluation of our theories of intelligence.

The same conclusion would seem to follow from the recent work of Lehrl (1980), Lehrl *et al.,* (1980), in Germany, who demonstrated that a very simple test requiring subjects to read aloud letters and numbers, and measuring the speed with which they performed the task, could produce very accurate estimates of intelligence, comparable to those provided by IQ tests. In all this work on reaction times, inspection times, or other simple sensory and motor tasks, it is apprehension of experience, rather than the eduction of relations and correlates, that is involved, and the high correlations obtained between these simple measures and IQ tests cannot easily be explained in terms of any existing theory of intelligence.

The construction of a theory encompassing all these diverse new facts may begin with a reconsideration of the old distinction, already apparent in Thorndike (1927), of power versus speed in IQ tests. This dichotomy is closely related to that between untimed and timed tests. Typically timed tests consist of items each of which could readily be solved by practically all subjects, given enough time; however, the test is timed, so that only a limited number of problems can be solved, the number depending on the speed with which the subject succeeds in performing the task. High IQ is here identified with speedy solution. Untimed tests, on the other hand, consist of items varying in difficulty level, with many of them too difficult to be solved by the majority of subjects. While theoretically one might have thought that these two rather different types of test might tap quite divergent mental abilities, in actual fact it has usually been observed that scores correlate highly together, suggesting that power is simply a function of speed (Berger, 1982). Furneaux (1960) has shown that there is logarithmic relation between time taken to solve a problem, and the difficulty level of that problem; for slow solvers the time needed for a more or less difficult problem increases so much that the problem becomes for all practical purposes insoluble, depending in part of course on the subject's persistence.

Furneaux developed a theory of intelligence which was based on Hick's Law (1952). As already mentioned, Hick had shown that the relationship between the time taken to react within a multiple-choice situation and the complexity of the choice stimuli could be expressed as: $RT = K \log M$, where RT is the choice reaction time, K an individual constant, and M a function of the complexity of the choice situation. He developed the argument that this is the relationship one would expect to observe if multiple-choice activity involves successive binary classifications. As the brain seems to consist of a vast number of nearly identical units, he suggested that all its activities might involve sequences of elementary operations of like kind and duration. Such a device might well function by carrying out successive binary switchings, with each 'switch' taking the same time and involving the same sort of simple basic activity. As Furneaux points out, 'this hypothesis of Hick's seems to imply that multiple-choice reaction-time is a measure of the time required for a search to be completed in the brain for the set of 'connections' which would initiate the required behaviour' (p.185). Furneaux went on to suggest that problem-solving could perhaps be regarded as a special case of a multiple-choice reaction, and that the rather striking characteristics of Hick's equation could be explained by postulating within problem-solving processes the repeated occurrence of some elementary activity which requires a substantially constant time for completion. He went on to develop a theory of intelligence involving a search process which brought into association a set of elements (perceptual or memory) relevant to the solution. He also postulated a 'comparator' — a device which carries out an examination of the results of this search, bringing together the neural representations of the perceptual material embodying the problem, the rules according to which the problem has to be solved, and the particular organisation of elements whose validity as a solution has to be examined.

It is interesting to note that this search hypothesis is a forerunner of many similar hypotheses later developed in the field of artificial intelligence (Newell and Simon, 1972, 1976; Newell, 1982). The similarity between brain processes and computers is of course already apparent in Hick's hypothesis, depending on the throwing of mental 'switches' which find a precise analogue in modern computers.

Jensen (1982) has further developed these hypotheses by pointing out that the conscious brain acts as a one-channel or *limited capacity* information processing system, a theory widely accepted in experimental psychology. It can deal simultaneously with only a very limited amount of information, thus restricting the number of operations that can be performed simultaneously on the information that enters the system from external stimuli or from retrieval of information stored in short-term or long-term memory. It follows that speediness of mental operations is advantageous in that more operations per unit of time can be executed without overloading the system.

A second important point is that there is rapid decay of stimulus traces and information, so that there is an advantage to speediness of any operations that must be performed on the information while it is still available. Thirdly, the individual compensates for limited capacity and rapid decay of incoming information by rehearsal and storage of the information into intermediate or long-term memory, which has relatively unlimited capacity, as compared with short-term memory which is very limited in this respect. However, the process of storing information in long-term memory itself takes time, and therefore uses up channel capacity, so that there is a trade-off between the storage and the processing of incoming information.

> 'The more complex the information and the operations required on it, the more time that is required, and consequently the greater the advantage of speediness in all the elemental processes involved. Loss of information due to overload interference and decay of traces that were inadequately encoded or rehearsed for storage or retrieval from LTM results in 'breakdown' and failure to grasp all the essential relationships among the elements of a complex problem needed for its solution. Speediness of information processing, therefore, should be increasingly related to success in dealing with cognitive tasks to the extent that the information load strains the individual's limited channel capacity. The most discriminating test items thus would be those that 'threaten' the information processing system at the threshold of 'breakdown'!
>
> 'In a series of items of greater complexity this 'breakdown' would occur at different points for various individuals. If individual

> differences in the speed of elemental components of information processing could be measured in tasks that are so simple as to rule out 'breakdown' failure, as in the several RT paradigms previously decribed, it should be possible to predict the individual differences in the point of 'breakdown' for more complex tasks' (Jensen, 1982, p.121-122).

In this way Jensen attempts to explain the observed correlations between RT variables and scores on complex g-loaded tests, and simultaneously the high correlations between speed and power tests.

Attractive as these theories may be, and although they undoubtedly encompass a good deal of relevant information and factual material, I believe that we must take a further step to explain these apparent differences in 'speediness' of mental processes. It seems unlikely, for physiological reasons, that mental speed is anchored in differential rates of propagation of nervous impulses, and although there may be a possibility of differential speed of processing through the synapses, an alternative hypothesis seems more likely, and better supported by factual investigations. This alternative hypothesis brings us to recent work on the psychophysiology of information processing, and through it to the latest results in the attempted reduction of a mentalistic concept like 'intelligence' to simple physiological processes and measures.

From the very beginnings of research involving the electroencephalograph, attempts have been made to relate different EEG patterns and intelligence, with little success on the whole. Knott *et al.* (1942) found a significant positive relationship between occipital alpha frequency and intelligence in 8-year-old children, but not on 12-year-old children. In the work of Netchine and Lairy (1960) both positive and negative correlations between alpha frequency and intelligence were found. Henry (1944) failed to find any correlations in a sample of 211 children of normal intelligence, aged 5-11 years. Bosaeus *et al.* (1977) found little correlation between broad band parameters of EEG activity and IQ as measured by the WISC Test. There was some suggestion of a slight negative correlation between IQ and theta power at parieto-occipital derivations, a result in agreement with the work of Henry (1944), but these relations are very slight. More recently Gasser *et al.* (1983), using computerised analysis of the EEG, found reasonably high correlation between the WISC and selected EEG parameters, particularly in mildly retarded children. However, on the whole the results are disappointing, difficult to explain theoretically, and do not help us much in our search for a new model of intelligence.

The same may be said about the early work on evoked potential (Callaway, 1975; Eysenck and Barrett, 1983). Figure 3 illustrates the nature of evoked potentials. These are waves of negative and positive potentials, observed on the electroencephalograph after a visual or auditory stimulus is given (at point A in the diagram), and superimposed on the ordinary fluctuations of the EEG. Evoked potentials have a poor signal-to-noise ratio, and hence 50-100 such potentials have to be recorded and averaged in order to achieve a meaningful and regular trace. Early work on evoked potentials showed that there are relatively small correlations (in the range of 0.2 to 0.3) between IQ on the one hand, and latency and amplitude of the evoked potentials, on the other. Correlations of IQ with latency are negative, i.e. the faster the waves follow each other, the higher is the IQ of the subject, while the correlations between IQ and amplitude are positive, i.e. the brighter the subject, the larger are the peaks and troughs of the evoked potential.

FIGURE 3

Diagrammatic representation of the Averaged Evoked Potential (AEP).

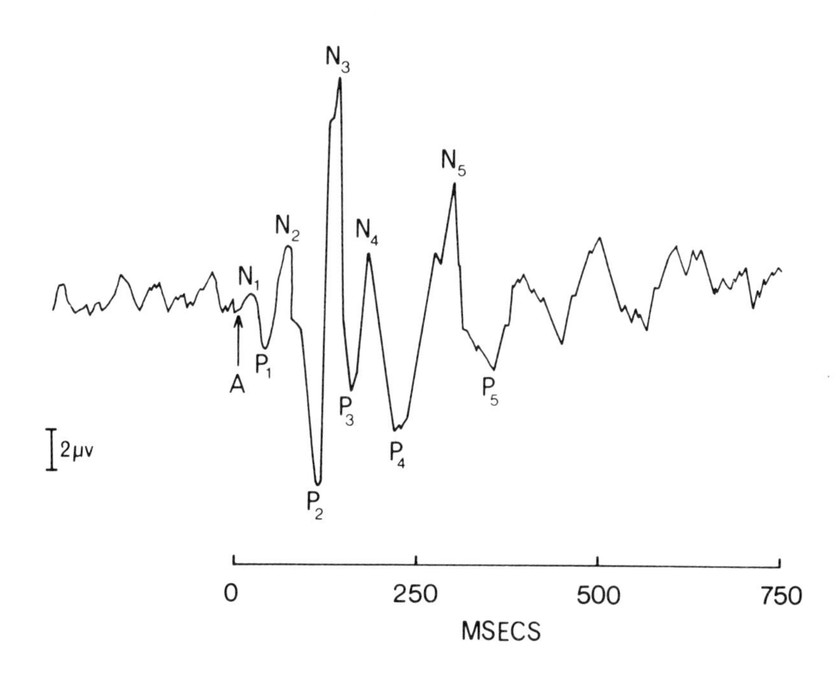

There is also a relationship between *variability* of the individual AEP (averaged evoked potential) records, latency and amplitude. As already mentioned, evoked potentials have to be averaged over a number of evocations (in the case of our own work, usually over something like 90 repetitions), and of course each repetition will be slightly different from all the others. The differences can be measured, showing that some individuals show greater variability than others. That being so, it must follow that if a person shows greater variability, the amplitude of his positive and negative potentials will be less, and the latency greater. The reason is of course that if variability is small, troughs on one evocation will be superimposed on troughs on another, thus adding to the amplitude. When two evocations are rather dissimilar, troughs may be superimposed on peak, and *vice versa,* thus reducing the amplitude. In a similar way, short latencies are only possible if all the evocations have short latencies; variability in latency will inevitably produce longer mean latencies. Thus we might regard variability as in some way more fundamental than either latency or amplitude, being capable of producing differences in both.

What, in turn, produces variability? Alan Hendrickson (1982) suggested a biochemical theory according to which pulse trains transmitting information through the cortex were liable to suffer errors in transmission, probably at the synapses. Any such error would cause a deviation from the 'true' evoked potential, and would hence reduce amplitude and increase latency. This is not the place to discuss a highly complex and advanced theory, proof or disproof for which must of course rest with biochemists and physiologists; however, the notion that errors in transmission are related to evoked potentials, and also inevitably to problem solving capacity, is an important and interesting one for the psychologist, and clearly deserves to be followed up.

Such a follow-up has been reported by Elaine Hendrickson (1982), who demonstrated on 219 more or less randomly selected 15-year-old school children that by using suitable measures of the evoked potential, derived

FIGURE 4

Scatter diagram showing relation between AEP and Wechsler IQ test (WAIS).

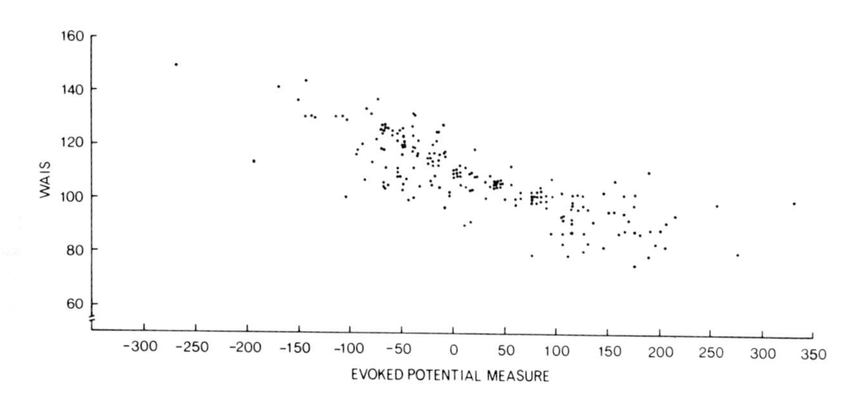

from the error hypothesis, a very high correlation could be demonstrated with Wechsler IQ. The actual observed correlation was 0.83, and figure 4 shows the actual scatter diagram, with the evoked potential score on the abscissa, and the IQ on the ordinate. Later work, replicating the findings on a different sample, have been reported by Blinkhorn and Hendrickson (1982). Correlations in excess of 0.80 between a simple physiological measure, requiring neither motivation nor any form of knowledge base, and an IQ test heavily dependent on motivation, knowledge, and test sophistication is sufficiently revolutionary to suggest that novel theories about the nature of intelligence are urgently required to take into account these findings. The fact that outside replications (e.g. Haier *et al.,* 1983) are available suggests that the results are not 'one off', non-replicable curiosa, but require to be taken seriously.

A rather different paradigm to the Hendrickson one has been advanced by Schafer (1982). This paradigm is based on studies showing the influence of selective attention and information processing workload on the amplitude of AEPs; this modulation is manifested as a tendency for unexpected or 'attended' stimuli to produce AEPs of larger overall amplitude than those generated using stimuli whose nature and timing is known by the individual. Schafer has extended the scope of this empirical phenomenon, hypothesising that individual difference in the modulation of amplitude (called by him 'cognitive neural adaptability') will relate to individual differences in intelligence. The physiological basis mediating this relationship is hypothesised to be neural energy as defined by the number of neurones firing in response to a stimulus. A functionally efficient brain will use fewer neurones to process a foreknown stimulus, whereas for a novel, unexpected stimulus, the brain will commit large numbers of neurones.

Given the relationship between individual neurone firing patterns and observed cortical AEPs, the commitment of neural energy will be observed as amplitude differences between AEPs elicited from various stimulus presentation conditions. Schafer defines his operational measures as variations around the concept of an individual's 'average amplitude'. Thus individuals with high neural adaptability, characterised by AEPs with much smaller than average amplitude to expected stimuli, and much larger than average amplitude to unexpected stimuli, should show high intelligence test performance. Conversely, for individuals with low neural adaptability, the size of such AEP amplitude modulation should be diminished, with a corresponding low intelligence test score. Empirical tests of this hypothesis have shown unusually high correlations between IQ and cognitive neural adaptability, thus supporting the Schafer hypothesis.

It may be possible, although with difficulty, to subsume the Schafer paradigm under the Hendrickson one, in the sense that if a repetitive stimulus is presented to an individual whose nervous system predisposes him to make errors in transmission, the repetitive stimulus may appear as a novel one. This may not be a likely hypothesis, but it is a testable one, and it is certain that there must be a common cause for the two phenomena (the Hendrickson and the Schafer one) because both correlate so highly with the third variable, namely IQ, that independence is statistically impossible.

There are other paradigms, such as the Robinson (1982; 1983) one, also suggesting different theories about the nature of the relationship between physiological measurement of brain events and IQ, but this is not the place to enter into a discussion of this very new and largely unexplored field. Eysenck and Barrett (1983) have reviewed the whole literature, and offered a critical summary of this work. Here we will assume that at the moment the Hendrickson paradigm is the best supported, and try rather to relate the theory of 'errors in transmission' to the emerging new model of intelligence.

Such a model can be constructed by making use of the theories already outlined which make mental speed responsible for differences in intelligence; what is needed, however, is an integration of speed and the Hendricksons' 'error hypothesis'. Surprisingly, this is a relatively easy task (Eysenck, 1982a). It is well known that messages transmitted through the nervous system are not transmitted in isolation, but repeatedly; this suggests that there must be incorporated in the nervous system a comparator which looks at these repeated messages and decides whether they are identical (and hence acceptable as representation of reality) or not (Sokolov, 1960, 1963, has advanced a similar hypothesis). Let us suppose, for the sake of the argument, that any particular 'message' is transmitted ten times, and that the comparator will accept it provided eight of the messages it receives are identical. In a person making a few errors, the first eight messages received would very likely be identical, and hence acceptable. In a person making many errors, it may take 20, 30, or more messages before the criterion is reached; hence he will be very much slower in his mental reactions, having to wait such a long time for the acceptance of the message as 'correct'. Hence correct processing of information is the fundamental variable, speed of mental processing is a secondary variable depending on errorless information processing. Given this relationship, all the comments made about mental speed naturally apply also to errorless transmission, and explain why errorless transmission is so important in solving mental problems.

The model of course differs in one important aspect from traditional models of thinking, in that it lacks an independent 'problem solver', a kind of homunculus which in most psychological theories lurks somewhere in the brain and receives messages, cogitates and solves problems, only to communicate the final solution to the subject. Obviously such a hypothetical entity is of no value in telling us anything about the nature of problem solving, as the question is simply aborted by the postulation of such an homunculus.

As we have already suggested, we can get rid of the homunculus by postulating a kind of search process which may be total and exhaustive, or heuristic (Newell and Simon, 1976). Much information has been acquired about the of such search processes by scientists interested in artificial intelligence, and computer programmes are available to demonstrate not only that these processes work, but also that they are similar in important ways to the events which occur during human problem solving (Newell and Simon, 1972). If it is possible, as they point out, to devise a computer programme for problem solving which depends on heuristic search and a comparator, then the obvious similarity of this arrangement and that suggested by Furneaux for the human problem solver does seem to argue that we may now be on the threshold of a theory of, not only the solution of problems, but also of differences in ability to solve these problems. It cannot be the point of this paper to develop these ideas in detail, but it must suffice simply to point out the direction in which progress has recently been made, and the ways in which it may proceed.

We may now return to our intelligence A, intelligence B and intelligence C. Intelligence A is the kind of intelligence Galton was concerned with, and recent work on reaction times, inspection times and in particular evoked potentials has amply justified his faith that intelligence A could be measured by simple physiological or semi-physiological means.

Intelligence B, the kind of intelligence Binet was concerned with, is obviously fundamentally based on intelligence A, but also incorporates differences in the knowledge base for different people, cultural and educational factors probably related to the knowledge base, personality factors, and much else besides. Intelligence B is clearly a conglomerate, the individual parts of which must be separated out and individually and separately measured in order to be susceptible to scientific investigation.

Intelligence C, the measurement of intelligence, is clearly also non-homogeneous, embracing on the one hand IQ tests of the Binet type intended to measure intelligence B, and remarkably successful in doing so (Eysenck, 1979), and on the other hand physiological tests like the evoked potential and reaction times, designed to measure intelligence A. The fact that these two sets of measures correlate so highly together (in excess of 0.80, as we have seen) suggests, as indeed much other research has shown, that the differences in intelligence A account for something like 80% of observed differences in intelligence B, at least in our type of culture, and in this century (Eysenck, 1979). It is well known that evoked potentials show a very strong hereditary determination, whereas for typical IQ tests heredity only counts for something like 80% of the variance (broad heritability, corrected for attenuation). The suggestion would therefore be that evoked potential records measure the innate, biological basis of intelligence B without the cultural, educational and generally environmental distortions inevitably found in IQ tests designed as measures of intelligence B.

The difference may become apparent in looking at some data on two groups of children, one group of 25 coming from high SES parents, and a group of 25 children coming from low SES parents (Eysenck, 1982a). The difference between them on Wechsler IQ was 1.64 standard deviations, and it was predicted that the difference (in standard terms) between the two groups would be less on the AEP measures of the EEG because on the Wechsler test part of the group difference in IQ would be contributed by environmental factors which would not be playing a part in the EEG measures. The two groups were found to be significantly less differentiated in terms of the EEG measure than the IQ, thus supporting the hypothesis. (Quantitative predictions of the amount of regression to be predicted are handicapped by a lack of knowledge of the precise heritability of the EEG measures, and should hence not be taken too seriously as they depend very much on estimates).

What has been said so far will be sufficient to indicate that there is indeed a revolution occurring in our conception of intelligence, a revolution that leads us back from Binet's type of approach to that pioneered by Sir Francis Galton. Galtonian concepts of intelligence have suffered a long decline, but the evidence here surveyed suggests that in his essentials Galton was right, and that we must postulate a general and largely innate factor of intelligence in order to explain the observed phenomena. Many practical consequences follow from this realisation, both for eugenics and also for applied psychology, and indeed for experimental psychology as well; it cannot be the task of this chapter to spell out these consequences. The revolution was needed primarily because most psychologists interested in the problems of intelligence used a psychometric, rather than experimental approach. The appropriate use of statistics in science is of course an essential part of methodology, but statistics must have a proper experimental basis in order to work properly, and this experimental basis has been largely missing in recent years (Eysenck, 1982a). Experimental studies have brought about the revolution, and the new concepts thus introduced require further experimental investigations to clarify the situation and put our new theories on a more secure basis.

References

Berger, M. (1982). The 'scientific approach' to intelligence: An overview of its history with special reference to mental speed. In *A Model for Intelligence,* edited by H.J. Eysenck. New York: Springer-Verlag.

Blinkhorn, S.F. and Hendrickson, D.E. (1982). Averaged evoked responses and psychometric intelligence. *Nature,* 295, 596-597.

Bosaeus, E., Matousek, M. and Petersen, I. (1977). Correlation between paedopsychiatric findings and EEG variables in well-functioning children of ages 6 to 16 years. *Scandinavian Journal of Psychology,* 18, 140-147.

Brand, C.R. and Deary, I.J. (1982). Intelligence and 'inspection time'. In *A Model for Intelligence,* edited by H.J. Eysenck. New York: Springer-Verlag.

Burt, C. (1909). Experimental tests of general intelligence. *British Journal of Psychology,* 3, 94-177.

Callaway, E. (1975). *Brain Electrical Potentials and Individual Psychological Differences.* London: Grune and Stratton.

Eysenck, H.J. (1953). *Uses and Abuses of Psychology.* London: Penguin Books.

Eysenck, H.J. (1979). *The Structure and Measurement of Intelligence.* New York: Springer-Verlag.

Eysenck, H.J. (Editor) (1982a). *A Model for Intelligence.* New York: Springer-Verlag.

Eysenck, H.J. (1982b). The sociology of psychological knowledge, the genetic interpretation of the I.Q., and Marxist-Leninist ideology. *Bulletin of the British Psychological Society,* 35, 449-451.

Eysenck, H.J. and Barrett, P. (1983). Psychophysiology and the measurement of intelligence. In *Methodological and Statistical Advances in the Study of Individual Differences,* edited by C.R. Reynolds and V. Willson. New York: Plenum Press.

Eysenck, H.J. and Eysenck, M.W. (1984). *Personality and Individual Differences.* New York: Plenum Press.

Furneaux, W.D. (1960). Intellectual abilities and problem-solving behaviour. In *Handbook of Abnormal Psychology,* edited by H.J. Eysenck. London: Pitman.

Gasser, T., Lucadou-Müller, I., Verleger, R. and Bächer, P. (1983). Correlating EEG and I.Q.: A new look at an old problem using computerized EEG parameters. *Electroencephalography and Clinical Neurophysiology,* 55, 493-504.

Guilford, J.P. and Hoepfner, R. (1971). *The Analysis of Intelligence.* New York: McGraw-Hill.

Haier, R.J., Robinson, D.L., Braden, W. and Williams, D. (1983). Electrical potentials of the cerebral cortex and psychometric intelligence. *Personality and Individual Differences,* in press.

Hendrickson, A.E. (1982). The biological basis of intelligence Part I. Theory. In *A Model for Intelligence,* edited by H.J. Eysenck. New York: Springer-Verlag.

Hendrickson, D.E. (1982). The biological basis of intelligence Part II. Measurement. In *A Model for Intelligence,* edited by H.J. Eysenck. New York: Springer-Verlag.

Henry, C.E. (1944). Electroencephalograms of normal children. *Monograph of the Society for Research in Child Development,* 39, No.9.

Hick, W. (1952). On the rate of gain of information. *Quarterly Journal of Experimental Psychology,* 4, 11-26.

Jensen, A.R. (1982). Reaction time and psychometric *g.* In *A Model for Intelligence,* edited by H.J. Eysenck. New York: Springer-Verlag.

Knott, J.R., Friedman, H. and Bardsley, R. (1942). Some electroencaphalographic correlates of intelligence in eight-year and twelve-year old children. *Journal of Experimental Psychology,* 30, 380-391.

Lehrl, S. (1980). Subjectives Zeitquant als missing link zwischen Intelligenzpsychologie und Neuropsychologie? *Grundlegens studient der Kybernetik und Geisteswissenschaft,* 21, 107-116.

Lehrl, S., Gallwitz, A. and Blaham, L. (1980). *Kurztest für allgemeine Intelligenz KAI: Manual.* Munich: Vless.

Netchine, S. and Lairy, G.C. (1960). Ondes cérébrales et niveau mental: quelques aspects de l'evolution génétique du tracé EEG suivant le niveau. *Enfance,* 4-5, 427-439.
Newell, A. (1982). The knowledge level. *Artificial Intelligence,* 18, 87-127.
Newell, A. and Simon, H.A. (1972). *Human Problem Solving.* Englewood Cliffs: Prentice-Hall.
Newell, A. and Simon, H.A. (1976). Computer science as empirical inquiry: symbols and search. *Communications of the ACM,* 19, 113-126.
Robinson, D.L. (1982). Properties of the diffuse thalamocortical system and human personality: a direct test of Pavlovian/Eysenckian theory. *Personality and Individual Differences,* 3, 1-16.
Robinson, D.L. (1983). Properties of the diffuse thalamocortical system, human intelligence and differentiated vs. integrated modes of learning. *Personality and Individual Differences,* 3, 393-405.
Rushton, P., Fulker, D.W., Neale, M. and Eysenck, H.J. (in press). Individual differences in human altruism are inherited. *Nature.*
Schafer, E.W.P. (1982). Neural adaptability: a biological determinant of behavioural intelligence. *International Journal of Neurosciences,* 17, 183-191.
Sokolov, E.N. (1960). Neuronal models and the orienting reflex. In *The Central Nervous System and Behaviour,* edited by M.A. Brazier. New York: J. Macy.
Sokolov, E.N. (1963). *Perception and the Conditioned Reflex.* Oxford: Pergamon Press.
Spearman, C.E. (1904). 'General intelligence' objectively determined and measured. *American Journal of Psychology* 15, 201-293.
Spearman, C.E. (1927). *Abilities of Man.* London: Macmillan.
Terman, L.M. and Oden, M.H. (1959). *The Gifted Group in Mid-life.* Stanford: Stanford University Press.
Thorndike, E.L. (1927). *The Measurement of Intelligence.* New York: Columbia University Press.
Thurstone, L.L. (1938). *Primary Mental Abilities.* Chicago: University of Chicago Press.
White, P.O. (1982). Some major components of general intelligence. In *A Model for Intelligence,* edited by H.J. Eysenck. New York: Springer-Verlag.
Wissler, C. (1901). The correlation of mental and physical tests. *Psychological Revue Monograph,* No.3.

Intelligence and Inspection Time: An Ontogenetic Relationship?

C. R. BRAND

Department of Psychology, University of Edinburgh, Edinburgh

It is now fifty years since the great American psychometrician, Louis Thurstone (1934) declared: 'It is my conviction that the isolation of the mental abilities will turn out to be essentially a problem in genetics.' By British standards — and particularly by the standards of the London School — Thurstone was something of a high-spirited American radical in his belief in the numerosity and independence of 'the mental abilities'; yet, unlike his many disunitarian followers in later years, he clearly held that the underlying causal realities of intelligence (whose discovery alone would help psychologists to understand, rather than merely to factor-analyse, their matrices of correlations) would be genetic.

Can General Intelligence be Both Unitary and Heritable?

In principle there need be no connection between a psychologist's beliefs as to the unitariness and as to the heritability of general intelligence (*g*). In practice, however, Thurstone's position is relatively unusual. Disunitarianism about *g* commonly goes hand-in-hand with environmentalism — and never more conspicuously than in the case of S.J. Gould (1981), who clearly execrates *g* and holds it to be 'the rotten core of Jensen's edifice, and of the entire hereditarian school'.

Such conventional conjunctions of beliefs are not without their stresses: (i) For all that an appeal to the influence of the environment on a rich diversity of forms of intelligence might be expected to detail the distinct effects of such domestic variables as affection, attention, stimulation, reinforcement, moral standards, income and so forth, it often seems that the champions of the environment prefer to roll all domestic and public social influences up into one enormous super-variable of 'deprivation *vs* privilege'. While lambasting others for their simplistic scientism, social-environmentalists can be surprisingly simplistic themselves. They may thus hope, perhaps, to escape the trap of 'the sociologist's fallacy' (Jensen, 1980) in which environmentalists find themselves obliged to predict impossibly great environmental influence on IQ once they have given each of its environmental correlates independent causal status. Yet the undue emphasis on only one dimension — the social-class dimension — of environmental variance is too simple and makes allowance neither for the influence of the intellectual levels of an individual's close acquaintances (especially his family — see Zajonc, 1983) nor for an individual's positive choice of his own *milieu* and involvements from among the possibilities that are available to him. (ii) A more remarkable and more long-lasting irony, however, is the conjunction that constitutes the other side of the coin — the conjunction between unitarianism and hereditarianism, the jerry-built construction (as Gould would have it) that has been the twentieth-century abode of the London School of differential psychology. For, to date, the only popular version of hereditarianism with regard to IQ has been one that invokes the influence of many genes — a figure of about one hundred is sometimes mentioned by psychogeneticists. (Certainly, nothing less than a goodly handful of discrete influences (whether genetic or environmental) is required to generate the well proportioned bell-shaped curve that — even if it is not quite as symmetrical as Burt would have had it (see Dorfman, 1978) — is itself held to attest the comparability of general intelligence with other biologically based traits such as height and weight). Thus the London School must apparently hold that *g* operates powerfully and unitarily to influence conceptually distinguishable abilities that would be empirically independent were it not for the influence of *g*; and yet it must hold at the same time that *g* is itself under many discrete causal influences. Why then, it might be asked, do these independent ontogenetic originators of *g*-differences not express themselves at all in test performances in their own right? Why do they not result, indeed, in a disunitarian picture of radically independent mental abilities?

There is probably only one way in which genuinely independent genetic influences might be constrained into operating as joint contributors to one final phenotypic variable while having little phenotypic visibility of their own. Such constraint would exist if most of such genetic influences operated only upon (or at least in accordance with) the prior phenotypic products of other genes in the system; and such a genetic state of affairs would seem to provide a natural basis for 'growth' — whether of a tree, of a limb, or of intelligence itself. However, such interactive growth, being more than simply additive at each stage, necessarily yields greater differentiation — a greater variety of phenotypic possibilities — at later stages of growth. Thus it is that, at higher levels of growth, continued linear development may itself be less noticeable than other, associated phenotypic variations that growth to a certain stage has itself made possible: the top of the tree may indeed, to the upward-looking observer, be quite occluded by the profusion of its branches.

To envisage *g* as causally underpinned by factors that impose upon each other in the course of development and which each make their distinctive contributions over different sections of the phenotypic ability range would always have made a certain psychometric good sense. In particular, it has often appeared that there are more distinguishable ability factors amongst subjects of relatively high levels of general intelligence: while, in subjects of average intelligence, intended measures of 'creativity' and 'field-independence' have seemed to be as much measures of *g* as of any more specific ability, amongst more intelligent subjects these same measures often make interesting distinctions that prove to be unrelated to *g* and to be sensibly related to other special abilities and to occupational and recreational interests (Hargreaves & Bolton, 1972; Vernon, 1972). However, the case for thinking of *g*'s genetic architecture (or, for that matter, of its environmental architecture) in terms of interactive and growth-dependent contributions has probably been strengthened by the facts that have lately emerged about the relations between intelligence and indices of mental speed — and especially of 'inspection time' (IT).

A Summary of Findings Concerning Inspection Time (IT) and IQ

Although Burt (1909) once did some pioneering work which related tachistoscopic dot-span to teachers' judgments of children's intelligence, studies of tachistoscopic apprehension in relation to intelligence began to proliferate only in the 1970s. While many such studies have suggested that dull and mentally subnormal subjects require longer exposure-durations if they are to make correct judgements of briefly presented material (see Nettelbeck and Brewer, 1981; Brand and Deary, 1982; Campione, Brown and Ferrara, 1982), particularly strong negative associations have been reported between intelligence and the ability to make perceptual discriminations that would normally be very easy but which are made difficult by extremely brief presentation (around 100 *ms*) and by the backward (and sometimes forward) 'masking' of the material so as to reduce its availability in a testee's iconic memory (Nettlebeck and Lally, 1976; Brand, 1981; Brand and Deary, 1982; Nettlebeck and Kirby, 1983/84).

The most commonly used test materials for IT have been the two lines (of the ratio 1.4:1) that Vickers and Nettelbeck had once suggested might allow the study of perception in the absence of what, in the terminology of signal detection theory, is called 'noise'. Typically, on each trial, testees are asked to attend to a fixation point, in the area of which the difference between the line lengths will shortly appear; after a few seconds the test stimulus is briefly exposed — the longer of the two vertical lines appearing either on the left or right; as soon as the allotted exposure duration has elapsed, the 'mask' (densely composed of many vertical lines) is presented in place of the stimulus and the testee is invited to make, at leisure, his or her judgment as to whether the longer line had appeared to the left or right of the fixation point. Typically, during each testing session, subjects are first presented with relatively easy discriminations — using exposure-durations of several hundred milliseconds; shorter durations are used subsequently, the tester's aim being to discover the shortest duration at which the subject is capable of making correct judgments on the great majority of trials. Generally — and certainly in the studies conducted in Adelaide and Edinburgh — it has proved easy to encourage subjects by suggesting that they are coping well with successive challenges; and subjects of all levels of intelligence have seemed to pay eager attention throughout sessions lasting around half an hour.

Four general and apparently uncontroversial results have emerged from studies of IT to date.

Relation between IT and low intelligence

There are now some twelve independent studies in which institutionalised subjects of low levels of intelligence (in the range IQ 40-70) have been compared with age-peers of normal, psychometrically tested intelligence. In every case, despite various procedural alterations, mentally subnormal subjects have required very much longer durations of exposure. Although some subjects of low intelligence require such long exposure-durations as to make them technically 'outliers' in comparison with subjects of normal intelligence, their results are not presently attributable to any obvious differences in approach to the task; and, amongst subjects of low levels of intelligence, their ITs often correlate quite highly with their differences in mental test performance (e.g. Hulme and Turnbull, 1983; Nettlebeck, 1984/85). Moreover, the removal of outliers does not greatly reduce the correlation between IQ and IT amongst subjects of below-average intelligence. Correlations between IT and IQ are not attributable to variations in visual acuity as measured by Snellen Test: in many reported studies subjects have been selected for good acuity; in other studies (Deary, 1980; Sharp, 1982) acuity has shown some relationship to IT but little to IQ. Although some subjects of normal intelligence sometimes perform poorly (or at least erratically) on IT, subnormal subjects hardly ever perform well. The best (near-normal) IT to have been recorded by an officially subnormal subject in Edinburgh was from a patient who seemed more hyperactive (and indeed engagingly comical) than mentally subnormal; and his IQ test results proved, when enquiry was made of the hospital, to have been markedly erratic across various occasions of testing (see Deary, 1980).

Reliability of IT

ITs are not greatly influenced by practice: Nettlebeck (1984/85) has found improvements of 30 per cent over six sessions, but reliability coefficients are around 0.70 over several weeks — and they were around 0.83 in the only study to date of auditory IT (Ireland, 1981). Special instructions designed to enhance attention have had little effect on subjects' ITs (Charman, 1979; Lally and Nettelbeck, 1980). Some of the sources of unreliability are known: it has been observed in both Adelaide and Edinburgh that some subjects come to adopt a strategy of watching for an apparent-movement cue as the mask replaces the stimulus — this cue being particularly noticeable when light-emitting diodes rather than a tachistoscope are used to deliver the test-stimuli. It is also realised that efforts to present IT tasks by means of a microcomputer's TV screen are bound to be particularly unreliable because the screen is only refreshed at around fifty times per second and may thus not present a stimulus for the duration that is specified by the experimenter. (Despite such problems one very simple programme (entitled ANTELOPE) which uses the APPLE microcomputer to present dashed horizontal lines has shown significant differences between young males of IQs around 90 and 115.) Extended practice involving the experience of thousands of trials — many of them followed by feedback over several weeks has been observed to allow marked improvements in individual subjects; but such intense exposure cannot account for the individual differences in the studies that are under discussion in the present review.

ITs of criterion groups

Various extreme groups have performed broadly in line with the hypothesis that IT is related to major intellectual variations in fluid intelligence. Several members of MENSA who have been tested by the author in Edinburgh have — with one exception — shown brief ITs. The one exception was a lady who was taking anti-epileptic medication and whose performance at her place of work had recently given rise to concern. Such medication has also been observed to depress AEP records into the low IQ range (Elaine Hendrickson, *p.c.*). At the other extreme of the intellectual range, elderly subjects show longer ITs (Charman, 1979; Nettelbeck and Brewer, 1981; Hogg, 1983); and several patients suffering senile dementia who were tested by the author as part of a drug trial for Organon required exposures of more than one full second even when no backward mask was used and when enlarged stimuli were presented by projector on to a screen in front of the subject.

Other versions of IT

Several studies have used other versions of IT testing. In Adelaide, Nettelbeck has experimented with single light-flashes (to the left or right of central fixation) as test-stimuli, and also with vibrotactile IT in which subjects have to decide which of their index-fingers was stimulated prior to all their fingers being vibrated. In Edinburgh, a 'tachistophone' has been used to present subjects with very brief bursts of square-wave tones of 880 and 770Hz (Deary, 1980): testees try to detect the order in which these tones are presented on any given trial; and the duration of the tones (which sound like clicks) is varied until a testee's IT is established.

Correlations between these IT indices and the original two-line version have been high — so long as a full range of subjects is involved; and correlations with IQ have been around −0.60 across normal ranges of IQ. Some theoretical difficulties have emerged in the use of these tasks. Thus Nettelbeck maintains that ITs from his vibrotactile procedure are too long to be interpretable within Vickers' original theory of the accumulation of perceptual information. Some subjects — including to date one Mensan — cannot discriminate the tachistophonic tones at their maximum duration of 900ms and may report themselves as being tone-deaf. It is not entirely clear whether subjects with marked disabilities should be omitted from correlations with intellectual measures. In a recent investigation by the author in California, tachistophonic performance correlated at −0.48 with AFQT scores of twenty young men having IQs around either 115 or 90; discarding the seven subjects who were unable to judge reliably at maximum exposure-durations, this correlation rose to −0.60. From the University of Texas at Austin, Willerman and his colleagues have likewise reported that 'rapid auditory discrimination' distinguishes between bright and normal undergraduates (Raz *et al.,* 1982); but here again there are a few interpretative problems — especially concerning occasionally observed equalization of the performance of high and normal IQ subjects when extremely brief auditory stimuli (around 5ms) have been used.

Altogether it is clear that the last few years have witnessed the discovery of measures of apparently simple and elementary forms of information-intake that have strong correlations with major variations in intelligence as traditionally and psychometrically conceived. At the same time there remain uncertainties as to how these correlations should be modelled and understood. While these results must prove challenging to those who maintain that psychometric intelligence is but 'academic intelligence' — and is even then but some kind of an average of unrelated, specific, culturally acquired skills — they may yet come to be understood as indicating strategic tricks of which high IQ subjects are capable rather than basic superiorities of high IQ subjects in passive, unconscious information-processing operations. Mental intake speed should not be identified with intelligence as conventionally measured; it may not even be the ontogenetic *fons* of *g:* but it is certainly sufficiently well correlated with *g* to provide testimony that *g* is as much associated with perception as it is with reasoning, knowledge and skilled performance.

Controversies Concerning IT and IQ

The range of IQs across which the IT/IQ correlation obtains

An important restriction on the interpretation of correlations between IT and IQ would undoubtedly arise if these correlations only occurred over some particular part of the IQ range — and especially if that part of the IQ range were one which embraced important differences in social disposal and treatment of people of different levels of intelligence. In the simplest case, it might even be possible to attribute poor ITs to the institutional handling or diet of the mentally subnormal.

To date there are some seven studies that enable the comparison of strengths-of-effect using similar IT testing procedures across different parts of the IQ range (Brand and Deary, 1982; Nettelbeck and Kirby,

1983/84); in addition there are three studies known to the present author in which little correlation has been found between IT and IQ for subjects having mean IQs of 121 (Vernon, 1981), 115 (Mackintosh, 1982; Cooper *et al,* 1982) and 117 (Hulme and Turnbull, 1983).

At present it is probably uncontroversial to say that intellectual differences among subjects of above-average intelligence have but a modest relationship with IT: for subjects above IQ 100, correlations of around −0.25 have been typical. At the same time it is clear that the IT/IQ correlation is not dependent upon the inclusion of mentally subnormal people in the IQ range that is under study; several of the Edinburgh studies observed strong correlations in the absence of subjects of less than IQ 70; and Nettelbeck and Kirby's (1983/84) view from their own work is that the evidence favours a step-function not at around IQ 70 but rather at around IQ 85 — with the result for the Adelaide series that the IT/IQ correlation for subjects of more than IQ 85 might be in the region of −0.35. Unfortunately, relatively few subjects of IQs from 86 to 100 have been involved in the Adelaide studies: thus even Nettelbeck and Kirby's 'normally distributed reduced sample' — constructed in an attempt to ask what is the IT/IQ correlation in the normal population — has only half the number of subjects that should be expected in this division of the IQ range. Some evidence of a specially strong relation ($r = -0.88$) between IQ and IT for subjects in the IQ range 86-100 is provided by Cooper *et al.'s (op cit)* study of children in Cambridge. Moreover a recent comparison by the author of the ITs (using a light-emitting diode display linked to an APPLE microcomputer) of twenty-two young men of normal or corrected vision and having IQs (as indicated by AFQT results) of around either 90 or 115 did find a significant difference in the usual direction, the correlation between IT and IQ being −0.51. Probably there is a linear relation between IT and IQ up to about IQ 110, but little relation beyond that point. (Certainly, in Nettelbeck's work, the omission of subjects of IQ >115 hardly reduces IT/IQ correlations at all.) Although there seems to be a particularly marked difference between subjects of above and below IQ 85, this effect is not as great as it is for measures of reaction time (including decision time and variance in decision times) which seem in Nettelbeck's work to have very little relation to IQ once testees of IQ >85 are omitted. As to Hulme and Turnbull's claim that 'the relation between IQ and IT in the normal population of children is much lower than some previous research may have suggested', three points should be considered: (1) Hulme and Turnbull's 'normal children' had a mean IQ of 117; (2) the reliability of their IT testing is not reported; (3) their children were compared only in terms of their IQs even though they ranged over five Mental Age levels that are distinguished in the Manual for the WISC-R.

The relation between IT and Mental Age

It would be convenient theoretically if the idea that initial processing speed is related to intelligence up to some above-average level of the latter could be translated into predictions with regard to Mental Age as well as in regard to IQ. Several recent empirical developments suggest that IT may indeed change in parallel with the changes in fluid intelligence that occur with growth and ageing. Amongst young children (of ages six to twelve years), recent studies by Nettelbeck and Wilson (1983) and, in Northern Ireland, by D. Scallon (1982, *p.c.*) have found correlations of about −0.60 between IT and raw scores on Cattell's Culture Fair Test of Intelligence. Another parallel with the results obtained with IQs is that some ITs are particularly low — low enough to be 'outliers' — amongst subjects of low Mental Age. (On the other hand the high variance of relatively dull subjects would be compatible with the hypothesis that their problems with IT tasks are not unitary: some dull subjects clearly perform far worse on IT than would be predicted for people of their Mental Ages in view of the general relations between IQ and IT.) Yet another parallel between IQ and Mental Age in relation to IT may be that good performance at IT tasks is a sufficient but not a necessary condition of above-average intellectual ability: in so far as this phenomenon is sometimes seen in IT studies it may merely reflect the fact that some bright subjects perform poorly at IT tasks because of poor acuity, medication or other specific factors; but the matter could certainly bear further investigation. It is possible that other forms of mental speed bear a closer relation to intellectual differences at higher chronological and mental ages (e.g. Keating and Bobbitt, 1978).

An important developmental question concerns how IT relates to intelligence in circumstances where the development of intelligence would commonly be considered to be disturbed. A study of deaf children in Edinburgh (Bain, 1983) has recently examined the possibility that the tendency of IT tasks to relate especially strongly to levels of verbal intelligence (see Brand and Deary, 1982) would be less marked in deaf children in whom verbal development is typically delayed and often found to be unrelated to other indices of intelligence. Use was made of the light-emitting diode display and of three mental tests that were thought by an expert in deafness to provide particularly satisfactory estimates of intelligence. Correlations between IT and these putative measures of intelligence were around −0.30 for the full range of children. However, it transpired that it was only for the children of below-average ability that the mental tests correlated positively amongst themselves; and, over this ability-range, the IT task correlated at around −0.60 with the mental tests. Even under unusual developmental conditions, it appears that IT is related to intelligence up to some level at which other factors possibly come into play and beyond which intelligence itself is less conspicuously unitary.

The nature of IT tasks

In view of the striking relations that obtain between IT and intelligence, questions necessarily arise as to the precise nature of IT problems and as to cognitive stratagems that might be responsible for their solution. It is clearly of interest that the IT task is perceptual rather than involving alphanumeric recognition or reasoning: it is at least a task such that it would have been of no surprise to most psychologists if intelligence were uncorrelated with it; and it is hard to think of any current form of education or socialization that is remotely directed to improving children's performance on this kind of task.

Introspective accounts have provided no obvious clue as to how good performance is reliably achieved. Subjects sometimes believe that they perform better by disobeying the tester's instruction (to attend to the central fixational cue) and by looking at one or other of the two line lengths as they appear; but the author's occasional attempts to get individual subjects to exhibit such demonstrable superiorities have been unavailing. In the light-emitting diode version, many competent subjects certainly report that they observe apparent movement; but such reports do not occur in the tachistoscopic version of the task; and, in the light-emitting diode version, some subjects make substantial improvements in their performance long after they have become aware of the possibility of using the clue that is provided by apparent movement.

Perhaps the most obvious feature of the task that calls for study is the involvement of masking. Both Nettelbeck (1984/85) and Saccuzzo *et al.* (1979) have carried out investigations of whether normal and retarded subjects are equally affected by masking — with the result that there appears to be no such systematic difference that distinguishes these groups. It has sometimes been suggested (Saccuzzo and Schubert, 1981) that masking is particularly disruptive to subjects of schizoid and psychopathic personalities. These matters were expressly investigated in Edinburgh by Sharp (1982), who did indeed find that high scorers on the Eysencks' Psychoticism scale needed particularly long exposures of the stimulus lines when they were backward-masked. An especially striking result, however, was that when the test-stimuli were forward-masked without being backward-masked the correlation between IT and Heim *et al.'s* (1978) Vocabulary Scale was even higher than in the more usual forward- and backward-masked version: for Sharp's twelve young adults (involving no mentally subnormal subjects) this IT/IQ correlation was −0.84, and −0.82 once visual acuity differences were partialled out. This result may provide a clue as to why the IT/IQ correlations in the Edinburgh studies have tended to be higher (in the negative direction) than those observed in Adelaide and perhaps elsewhere. Because only a three-field tachistoscope has been available in Edinburgh, all the Edinburgh studies have unintentionally used a forward mask because the same field of the tachistoscope had to be used to present both the mask and the fixational cue.

IT and IQ: the Direction of Causation

It is clearly impossible at present to rule out the hypothesis that it is a person's level of *g* that equips him to be a competent performer on tests of IT — though particularly high levels of *g* clearly convey no marked superiorities on such tests. On the other hand, if it is a ready ability to apprehend the most simple perceptual realities that constitutes one major psychological and ontogenetic basis for the development of intelligence, it seems that enhanced powers of apprehension of the IT type convey no advantage beyond a certain level. Certainly there are some possible ways of probing the possibility that it is a subject's general level of cognitive overload that may interfere with his perceptual abilities — whether that overload stems from orectic features or from purely cognitive limitations: thus Nettelbeck (1984/85) reports that the IT's of subnormal subjects are particularly impaired if they are required to give their responses with two fingers of one hand rather than with the index fingers of their two hands; and Morrison (1982) has suggested that the interval between the onset of the attentional cue and the presentation of the test stimulus is a critical variable that may account for individual and developmental differences. Nevertheless, the studies that have been reviewed here clearly show a link between a relatively simple perceptual task and major individual differences in abilities on psychometric tests that have long provided, for whatever more complex reasons, broadly acceptable indices of individual differences in general intelligence. Those cognitive psychologists who have liked to say that 'intelligence is an abstraction and does not have a cause' (Hunt, 1983) now have a manageable problem upon which they can focus their analytical endeavours: should they be reluctant to say that there is now a serious lead as to what is the information processing basis of general intelligence, they could at least turn their thoughts from the question of 'What is intelligence?' to the question of 'What is Inspection Time?'. So long as their reconceptualizations do not merely take the form of replacing *g* with nominal substitutes such as 'attentional resources' (Hunt, 1980) and 'immediate arousal' (Sanders, 1977), it can be reasonably expected that such enquiries will bring several legendary social-scientific questions within the grasp of natural science.

At least it is clear that the reported IT/IQ correlations do not lend themselves to being explained as socio-cultural constructions that reflect Western capitalism's demands for and differential stimulation of 'academic intelligence'. Moreover, if mental intake speed (itself perhaps deriving from individual differences in the reliability of nervous transmission, as envisaged by Eysenck in this volume) cannot be said to be crucial to individual differences throughout the entire IQ range, this will at least make a certain amount of genetic sense. As my former student and co-worker, Dr Ian Deary, once put it to me, the relation between mental intake speed and intelligence may resemble the relation between income and patterns of investment and expenditure. Across the lower ranges of income there are fairly predictable relations between a person's income and his possessions; but, as the higher ranges of income are reached, big individual differences arise in the disposal of income — into luxuries, education, health care, addictions and so on. If intelligence is indeed polygenic and yet to an important degree unitary, it bears genetic consideration that those genes for intelligence that themselves make no difference to mental intake speed have their action by modifying and building upon a basis that has been provided — in some, if not all people — by a previous development of a capacity for apprehending quite basic aspects of reality.

Acknowledgments

For their help in arranging, conducting or apprising me of various of the studies newly mentioned above, I would like to indicate my gratitude to Peter Caryl, Hamish Macleod, David Wight, George Montgomery, Bernard Rimland, Jerry Larsen, Ted Nettelbeck, N.J. Mackintosh, A.R. Jensen, P.A. Vernon, Mark Strong and Diarmuid Scallon.

References

Bain, M. (1983). *Computerised Visual Inspection Time in a Sample of Deaf Children.* Final Honours Thesis: University of Edinburgh, Department of Psychology.

Brand, C.R. (1981) General intelligence and mental speed: their relationship and development. In *Intelligence and Learning,* M.P. Friedman, J.P. Das and N. O'Connor. New York: Plenum Press.

Brand, C.R. and Deary, I.J. (1982). Intelligence and 'Inspection Time'. In *A Model for Intelligence,* edited by H.J. Eysenck. New York: Springer-Verlag.

Burt, C. (1909). Experimental tests of general intelligence. *British Journal of Psychology,* 3, 94-177.

Campione, J.C. Brown, Ann L., and Ferrara, Roberta A. (1982). Mental retardation and intelligence. In *A Handbook of Human Intelligence,* edited by R.J. Sternberg. Cambridge: Cambridge University Press.

Charman, D.K. (1979). The ageing of iconic memory and attention. *British Journal of Social and Clinical Psychology,* 18, 2, 257-258.

Cooper, T., Cumberland, N., and Downing, M. (1982). Part II Project Report. Department of Psychology, University of Cambridge.

Deary, I.J. (1980). *How General is the Mental Speed Factor in 'General' Intelligence?* Final Honours Thesis: University of Edinburgh, Department of Psychology.

Dorfman, D.D. (1978). The Cyril Burt question: new findings. *Science,* 201, 4362, 1177-1186.

Gould, S.J. (1981). *The Mismeasure of Man.* New York: Norton.

Hargreaves, D.J. and Bolton, N. (1982). Selecting creativity tests for use in research. *British Journal of Psychology,* 63, 3, 451-462.

Heim, A.W., Watts, P.K. and Simmonds, V. (1978). *Manual for AH Vocabulary Scale.* Windsor, U.K: National Foundation for Educational Research.

Hogg, Lorna, I. (1983). *The Psychological Correlates of Ageing: Inspection Time, Intelligence, Cognitive Failures and Personality.* Final Honours Thesis: University of Edinburgh, Department of Psychology.

Hulme, C., and Turnbull, Jennifer (1983). Intelligence and inspection time in normal and mentally retarded subjects. *British Journal of Psychology,* 74, 3, 365.

Hunt, E. (1980). Intelligence as an information-processing concept. *British Journal of Psychology,* 71, 4, 449-474.

Hunt, E. (1983). On the nature of intelligence. *Science,* 219, 4581, 141-146.

Ireland, Christine (1981). *Inspection Time and the Intellectual Biorhythm.* Final Honours Thesis: University of Edinburgh, Department of Psychology.

Jensen, A.R. (1980). *Bias in Mental Testing.* London: Methuen.

Keating, D.P. and Bobbitt, B.L. (1978). Individual and developmental differences in cognitive components of mental ability. *Child Development,* 49, 155-167.

Lally, M. and Nettelbeck, T. (1980). Intelligence, reaction time and inspection time. *American Journal of Mental Deficiency,* 82, 273-281.

Mackintosh, N.J. (1982). Personal communication.

Morrison, F.J. (1982). The development of alertness. *Journal of Experimental Child Psychology,* 34, 2, 187-199.

Nettelbeck, T. (1984/85). Inspection time and mild mental retardation. *International Review of Research in Mental Retardation.* New York: Academic Press.

Nettelbeck, T. and Brewer, N. (1981). Studies of mild mental retardation and timed performance. *International Review of Research in Mental Retardation,* 10. New York: Academic Press.

Nettelbeck, T. and Kirby, N.H. (1983/84). Measures of timed performance and intelligence. *Intelligence,* in press.

Nettelbeck, T. and Lally, M. (1976). Inspection time and measured intelligence. *British Journal of Psychology,* 67, 17-22.

Nettelbeck, T. and Wilson, C. (1983). Developmental differences in inspection time. (In preparation)

Raz, N., Willerman, L., Ingmundson, P. and Hanlon, M. (1982). Aptitude-related differences in auditory recognition masking. (Available from L. Willerman, Department of Psychology, University of Texas at Austin).

Saccuzzo, D.P., Kerr, M., Marcus, A., and Brown, R. (1979). Input capability and speed of processing in mental retardation. *Journal of Abnormal Psychology,* 88, 341-345.

Saccuzzo, D.P., and Schubert, D. (1981). Backward masking as a measure of slow processing in schizophrenia spectrum disorders. *Journal of Abnormal Psychology,* 90, 305-312.

Sanders, A.F. (1977). Structural and functional aspects of the reaction process. In *Attention and Performance VI,* edited by S. Dornic. Hillsdale, New Jersey: Lawrence Erlbaum.

Sharp, D.M. (1982). *Inspection time, Intelligence and Information-processing Theory.* Final Honours Thesis: University of Edinburgh, Department of Psychology.

Thurstone, L.L. (1934). The vectors of mind. *Psychological Review,* 41, 1, 1-32.

Vernon, P.A. (1981). *Speed of Information Processing and General Intelligence.* Ph.D. Thesis: University of California at Berkeley.

Vernon, P.E. (1972). The distinctiveness of field-independence. *Journal of Personality,* 40, 366-391.

Zajonc, R.B. (1983). Validating the confluence model. *Psychological Bulletin,* 93, 3, 457-480.

Twin Studies of Intelligence: Recent Data, New Questions

J.K. HEWITT and K.A. LAST
Departments of Psychology and Genetics, University of Birmingham, Birmingham

The scientific study of twins as a means towards unravelling the interplay of nature and nurture probably began with the publication by Sir Francis Galton, in 1875, of a paper entitled 'The history of twins as a criterion of the relative powers of nature and nurture'. In this paper, Galton noted the occurrence of the two kinds of twins which we now call monozygotic or identical, and dizygotic or fraternal. He wrote:

> 'The consequence of this was a curious discontinuity in (his) results. One would have expected that twins would commonly be found to possess a certain average likeness to one another . . . but this is not at all the case. Extreme similarity and extreme dissimilarity between twins of the same sex, are nearly as common as moderate resemblance. When the twins are a boy and a girl, they are never closely alike; in fact, their origin is never due to the development of two germinal spots in the same ovum'.

In other words, opposite sex twins who must be dizygotic are not more alike than brother and sister while same sex twins may either be identical genetically or, if resulting from the independent fertilisation of two ova, again no more alike than ordinary siblings.

Since those initial insights, the twin method has been the cornerstone of human behaviour genetics. In part this is due to the clarity with which a preliminary analysis of the 'natural experiment' of twinning can be formulated and we will begin our discussion with an outline of the conceptual basis of the twin method. We will ask both what the method can tell us and what are its limitations while looking more closely at three important recent presentations of data on human intelligence. The first brings together all the available studies which have reported correlations in general intelligence for twins and other family pairings (Bouchard and McGue, 1981). The second reports data from the major longitudinal study of mental development in twins from birth to six years (Wilson, 1978), and the third applies the new extended twin-family designs in the detection of maternal effects in the development of human intelligence (Rose, Boughman, Corey, Nance, Christian and Kang, 1980). We will try to emphasise how too rigid a distinction between genetic and environmental effects may hinder rather than assist our understanding of the causes of human variation.

The Twin Method

Why have twins formed the basis of the study of human variation since Galton first described their potential? The key point for genetic studies is that identical twins have identical genes while fraternal twins share on average only half their genes. It follows that if identical twins are more alike than fraternal twins, then part of the variability seen in the population may be due to heritable differences.

The children of any human family share the same pool of parental genes, but each family has a different pool of parental genes. Thus, there is a source of genetic variation in the population for which related individuals are alike and different from individuals in unrelated families; we will call this G_1. However, within a family of siblings each individual draws a random set of genes from the parental pool — the processes of recombination and random assortment of chromosomes during the formation of egg and sperm ensure that each sibling draws a unique set. This source of genetic variation within families we will call G_1.

Similarly, members of a family may share a common environment which is different from that of other families. We call the effects of this E_2. However, even within a family individuals differ in their environmental experiences and we call this source of variation within families E_1. We may now ask how these four sources of variation contribute to the similarities and differences among individuals from pairs of identical and fraternal twins.

From Table I we can see that there is no source of genetical variation within identical twin pairs and so both G_1 and G_2 contribute to their similarity. The only differences within the pair are due to their individual experiences, E_1. If we now look at fraternal twins raised together, E_2 contributes to their similarity and E_1 to the differences between them. However, they now differ because of genetic segregation and so G_1 contributes to the differences.

If we assume a simple additive genetic system without more complex effects, then $G_1 = G_2$ and the sum of G_1 and G_2 is the total additive genetic variation which is specified as ½ D_R (Mather and Jinks, 1982). In the absence of E_2, we expect the similarity of identical twins to be double that of fraternal twins. This comparison provides a simple indication of the ability of E_1 and D_R to explain the variation. But we must be aware of other factors. For example, it is well known that people tend to choose mates similar to themselves in intelligence. This is called assor-

TABLE I

Expectations of a simple model for the similarity and differences of identical and non-identical twins

	Identical	Non-identical
Similarity	$G_1 + G_2 + E_2$	$G_2 + E_2$
Difference	E_1	$G_1 + E_1$

Note: $G_1 = 1/4\ D_R + 3/16\ H_R$
$G_2 = 1/4\ D_R + 1/16\ H_R + M$

where: $1/2\ D_R$ = total additive genetic variation
$1/4\ H_R$ = variation due to dominant and recessive genes
M = additive genetic variation due to assortative mating.

tative mating and its consequence will be increased additive genetic variation between families which we have called M and which inflates G_2. Conversely, the effect of dominant and recessive genes, an effect we label ¼ H_R, will tend to inflate G_1 compared with G_2. If we have data on twins raised together, we can only estimate three sources of variation at most and so immediately we have to make simplifying assumptions. For example, we might assume that there were no common family environmental effects, E_2, or that $G_1 = G_2$. However, with appropriate methods of analysis (Eaves, Last, Young and Martin, 1978), serious failure of these assumptions may be detected.

In summary, twins are a good starting point for studying variation because they provide powerful tests of simple models. In addition, they provide the best tests for certain more complex genetical and environmental effects, in particular for environmental sensitivity, competitive effects and sex-related effects (Eaves et al., 1978). Genetic and environmental models may be extended to other sorts of relationships which may be used to overcome most of the limitations of the twin design. With this in mind, we have examined the extensive set of data summarised by Bouchard and McGue (1981).

A Genotype and Environmental Model for IQ

Bouchard and McGue (1981) brought together 111 studies identified from the literature on familial resemblance in measured intelligence. From these we have extracted the correlations of twins and siblings raised together and apart and of unrelated individuals raised by adoptive parents, which can be specified in terms of our simple model. The original data are summarised in Figure 1.

Clearly there is considerable heterogeneity in the data as we would expect from a compilation of studies using different tests in different populations at different times. However, we have taken the weighted average correlation computed by Bouchard and McGue as our best estimate of the correlation for each family group. The particular pairings used and their expectations in terms of our model are shown in Table II. You will notice that the model predicts that fraternal twins reared together (DZ_T) should have the same correlation as full sibs (FS_T).

TABLE II

Family pairings considered in detail

Group	Pairings	Correlation	G_1	G_2	E_1	E_2	Twin Effect
Identical twins raised together	4672	0.86	1	1	0	1	1
Identical twins raised apart	65	0.72	1	1	0	0	1
Non-identical twins raised together	5546	0.60	0	1	0	1	1
Sibs raised together	26473	0.47	0	1	0	1	0
Sibs raised apart	203	0.24	0	1	0	0	0
Adopted/natural sib pair	345	0.29	0	0	0	1	0
Adopted/adopted sib pair	369	0.34	0	0	0	1	0
Husband/wife	3817	0.33					

To illustrate how we can easily be led into an over-simplified account of variation, when we have data on only a few relationships, we compare the conclusions that can be drawn from two sub-sets of these correlations with those from the full set.

The correlations and simple model for the most common sort of twin study, that of identical and fraternal twins raised together, are shown in Table III. We can estimate only two effects from these correlations with E_1 being given by the remaining variation, i.e. $E_1 = 1 - rMZ_T$.

FIGURE 1

Familial correlations for IQ (From Bouchard and McGue, 1981). Reprinted by permission from **Science**, *212, 1056. Copyright © 1981 AAAS.*

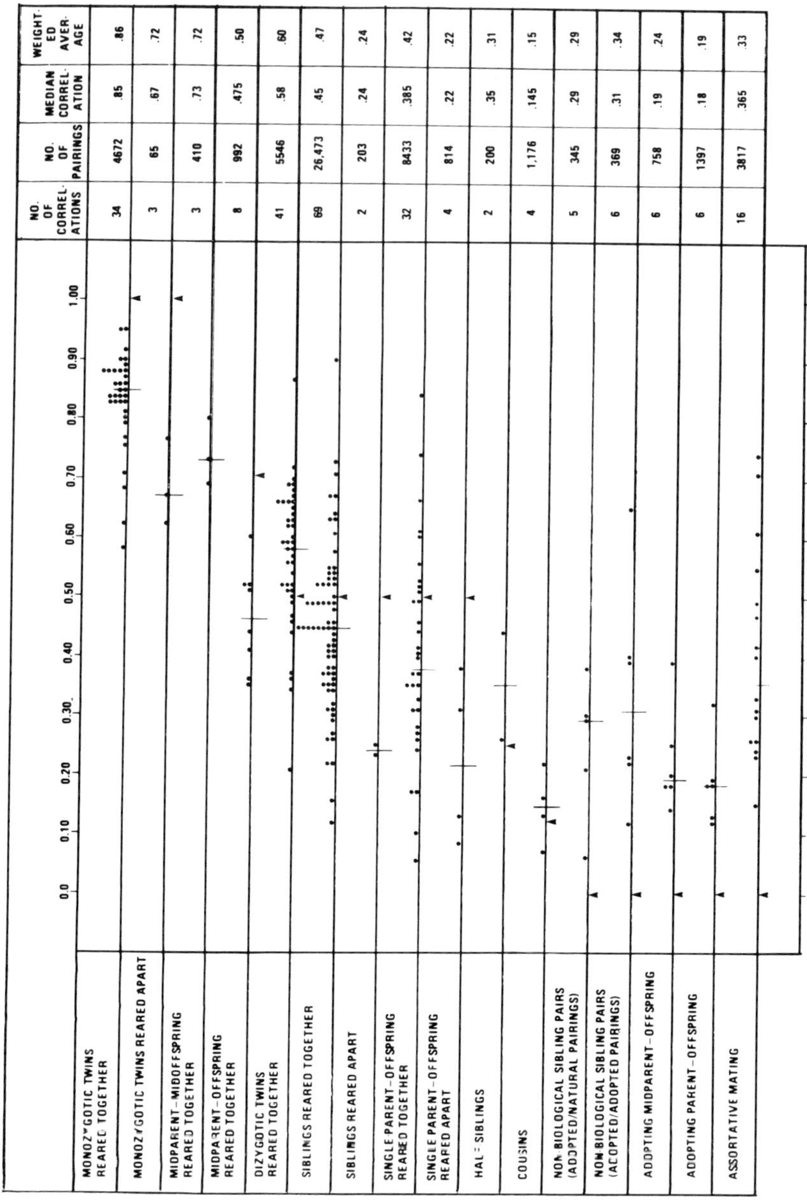

	NO. OF CORRELATIONS	NO. OF PAIRINGS	MEDIAN CORRELATION	WEIGHTED AVERAGE
MONOZYGOTIC TWINS REARED TOGETHER	34	4672	.85	.86
MONOZYGOTIC TWINS REARED APART	3	65	.67	.72
MIDPARENT–MIDOFFSPRING REARED TOGETHER	3	410	.73	.72
MIDPARENT–OFFSPRING REARED TOGETHER	8	992	.475	.50
DIZYGOTIC TWINS REARED TOGETHER	41	5546	.58	.60
SIBLINGS REARED TOGETHER	69	26,473	.45	.47
SIBLINGS REARED APART	2	203	.24	.24
SINGLE PARENT–OFFSPRING REARED TOGETHER	32	8433	.385	.42
SINGLE PARENT–OFFSPRING REARED APART	4	814	.22	.22
HALF SIBLINGS	2	200	.35	.31
COUSINS	4	1,176	.145	.15
NON-BIOLOGICAL SIBLING PAIRS (ADOPTED/NATURAL PAIRINGS)	5	345	.29	.29
NON-BIOLOGICAL SIBLING PAIRS (ADOPTED/ADOPTED PAIRINGS)	6	369	.31	.34
ADOPTING MIDPARENT–OFFSPRING	6	758	.19	.24
ADOPTING PARENT–OFFSPRING	6	1397	.18	.19
ASSORTATIVE MATING	16	3817	.365	.33

TABLE III

The model for twins raised together

The correlations and simple model

Group	*n*	*r*	G_1	G_2	E_1
Identical twins raised together	4672	0.86	1	1	0
Non-identical raised together	5546	0.60	0	1	0

The estimates for the simple model

$G_1 = 0.26 \pm 0.0094$

$G_2 = 0.60 \pm 0.0086$ No goodness of fit test possible

$E_1 = 0.14 \pm 0.0002$ Genetic variation accounts for 86%

Estimates for model describing type of genetic variation.

$\frac{1}{2} D_R = 0.52 \pm 0.0376$

$E_2 = 0.34 \pm 0.0176$ No goodness of fit test possible

$E_1 = 0.14 \pm 0.0002$ Genetic variation accounts for 52%

Because we have only two correlations and are estimating two effects, we have no test for the adequacy of the model. The estimates given in the table might suggest that genetic effects accounted for 86 per cent of the variation. However, if there is E_2 or assortative mating these will be included as part of G_2 and we notice that G_2 is greater than G_1. If we now assume that the genetic variation is simple and additive we can estimate ½ D_R and E_2 as 0.52 and 0.34 respectively (see Table III), suggesting that only 52 per cent of the variation is genetic. This dramatically shows the ambiguity of such a simple data set.

If we include the data for full siblings reared apart (FS_A), we can estimate up to 3 parameters; the correlations, model and estimates are shown in Table IV. These results suggest that the second of our two interpretations of the twin data alone is more plausible. Indeed, if we make the same simplifying assumptions as before, we find that ½ D_R = 0.52 and E_2 = 0.34 but this time we have a statistical test for the

TABLE IV

The model for twins raised together and siblings raised apart

The correlations and simple model

Group	n	r	G_1	G_2	E_1	E_2
Identical twins raised together	4672	0.86	1	1	0	1
Non-identical twins raised together	5546	0.60	0	1	0	1
Siblings raised together	203	0.24	0	1	0	0

The estimates for the simple model

$G_1 = 0.26 \pm 0.0094$

$G_2 = 0.24 \pm 0.0663$ No goodness of fit test possible
Simpler models were inadequate

$E_1 = 0.14 \pm 0.0002$ Genetic variation accounts for 50%

$E_2 = 0.36 \pm 0.0669$

Estimates for model describing type of genetic variation

$\frac{1}{2} D_R = 0.52 \pm 0.0372$ Goodness of fit test shows model is adequate

$E_2 = 0.34 \pm 0.0174$ (Chisquare on 1 d.f. = 0.09; $p = 0.76$)

$E_1 = 0.140 \pm 0.0002$ Genetic variation accounts for 52%

adequacy of this simple model and this shows that it explains the observed pattern of variation very well. But again we had only a limited data set and we know that this explanation is probably an oversimplification because, for example, there is correlation between husbands and wives suggestive of assortative mating.

To resolve this we turn to our full data set of seven correlations with the result of weighted least squares modelling (Eaves *et al,* 1978) shown in Table V. Our simple models failed to explain the full set of data, as we suspected earlier, because fraternal twins are significantly more alike than ordinary siblings. After trying various alternative models, the most plausible explanation invokes a special environmental effect which results

TABLE V

The model for the full data set of seven correlations

The estimates for the modified simple model		
G_1	= 0.26 ± 0.0094	Goodness of fit test shows this model is adequate
G_2	= 0.19 ± 0.0291	(Chisquare on 3 d.f. = 5.00; p = 0.17)
E_1	= 0.14 ± 0.0002	Simpler models were inadequate
E_2	= 0.28 ± 0.0298	Genetic variation accounts for 45%
Twin Effect	0.13 ± 0.0098	

The estimates from the model describing type of genetic variation		
½ D_R	= 0.24	
M	= 0.02	
¼ H_R	= 0.19	Genetic variation accounts for 45%
E_2	= 0.28	Additive genetic variation accounts for 26%
E_1	= 0.14	
Twin Effect	= 0.13	

in twins of either kind exhibiting additional similarities to those we would normally expect. Only now do we have a model which explans the data and it suggests that 45 per cent of the variation is genetic. Taking account of assortative mating, we can interpret G_1 and G_2 in terms of ½ D_R, ¼ H_R and M as shown in Table V. The genetic variation accounts for 45 per cent of the total, but only as little as 26 per cent is ascribable to additive genetic effects. The difference between these two figures is apparently due to complete genetic dominance.

This analysis raises as yet unresolved questions about the sources of twin similarity and confirms our reservations about the use of limited data sets, especially when based on twins alone who have in many respects unusual pre- and post-natal environments. However, the more extensive analyses require data sets that are unlikely to be obtained for anything other than, say, postal questionnaires, simply because of the enormous costs involved. As in the case of IQ, we will probably end by pooling heterogenous data collected over a long time period by different researchers to arrive at our best overall model, a clearly unsatisfactory situation. It has not been our intention to undermine the central role that the classical twin study must continue to play in human behaviour genetics; rather, we have tried to show how, given the appropriate resources, more general analyses might deepen our understanding of the nature of the genetic effect whose hypothesised presence is first put to the test by the twin study.

Viewed in this light, the twin study remains a first step in any research programme, and one example of its value is provided by work on the development of intelligence. Here, the combination of the longitudinal study with the power of the twin design for testing at least the simplest models takes us towards an understanding of the genetic and environmental control of the developmental sequence. The study which has attempted this challenging analysis has recently been reported upon by Wilson (1977, 1978).

The Development of intelligence

The twins in the Louisville Study are tested at 3 monthly intervals during their first year of life, then half yearly to 2 years and annually thereafter. From 3 months to 2 years the Bayley Scales of Infant Development are administered on each visit, at 2½ and 3 years the Stanford-Binet Form L-M and then the Weschler Preschool and Primary Scales at 4, 5 and 6 years. (For recent samples the McCarthy Scales of Children's Abilities have been used at the 4 year visit). A Mental Development Index is computed on a standardised scale (Wilson, 1977).

The first question of interest is the relative similarities of identical (MZ) and fraternal (DZ) twins tested at such young ages. The data reported by Wilson (1978) are summarised in Figure 2.

The superficial impressions are, firstly, that twins, whether identical or fraternal, are on average quite similar to each other in mental development from as early as 3 months and that this degree of similarity is maintained throughout the developmental sequence.

Secondly, the MZ and DZ degrees of similarity appear to track towards the adult values for general intelligence of around 0.86 and 0.60 respectively which we used in our previous analysis. However, although we have so far been obliged to work with correlations, where we have the necessary information a more powerful analysis is provided by a direct consideration of the variation between and within pairs from the standard analysis of variance (Eaves, *et al.,* 1978). Fortunately, Wilson (1978) provides sufficient information for us to reconstruct the relevant statistics and to attempt to fit models to these.

We first considered an environmental model which attributes all variation within pairs to environmental sources acting on individuals (E_1) and the apparent similarity of pairs to environmental variation which makes one family different from another (E_2).

With the exception of the 4 year old data, this simple model fails to account for the patterns of variation even at the earliest ages where a superficial examination of the correlations would have suggested this model as appropriate. The reason for this failure is that, on a simple

FIGURE 2

Correlations for MZ and DZ twins' mental development from 3 months to 6 years. (Adapted from Wilson, 1978).

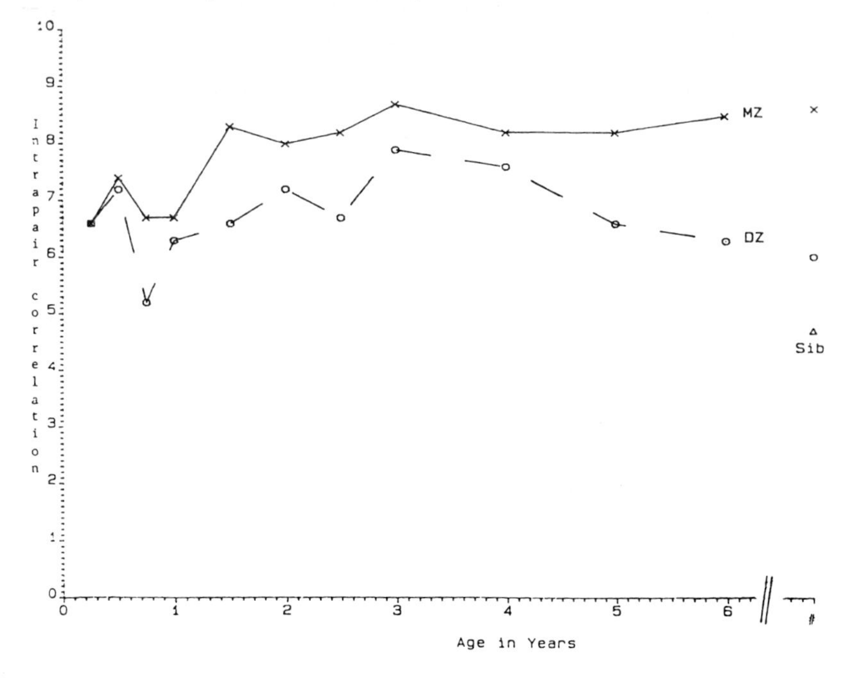

model, the total amount of variation for MZ and DZ twins should be the same. In this sample the total variance of DZ twins exceeds that for MZ twins by over 50 per cent at the younger ages.

The next model we tried was the simplest genetic model which says that all variation is due to additive genetic deviations (½ D_R), and individual environmental experiences E_1. Here again, with one exception at 9 months, the model was found to be inadequate.

We then went on to consider two more complex models. The first straightforwardly enough allowed simultaneously for all three of the sources of variation already considered. The second was motivated by the observation of discrepant total variances for the MZ and DZ twins and allowed for the possibility of competition or co-operation between twins (Eaves, 1976). This model recognises that within a twin pair, or any other sibship for that matter, an important aspect of one individual's environment may well be the influence of the other individual.

In the event, the model which best fitted the data, although rather poorly at the very young ages, was not one involving these sibling effects but the more traditional model, the results of which are presented in Table VI.

The main trends are easily summarised. For very young children, up to a year old, there is a considerable amount of variation which is either due to idiosyncratic environmental experiences (not shared with the twin) or, of course, unreliability of assessment. As development progresses this source of variation does not increase and probably declines. Thus, there is no evidence here that individual learning experiences, on which a behaviourist account would place emphasis, contribute in a cumulative sense to the rate of mental development in preschool children. As far as individual differences within families are concerned, genetic factors are at least as important as environmental factors from the first year of life onwards.

TABLE VI

Summary of model fitting to twin variation in mental development from birth to six years

Age	Percentage of variation			Goodness of fit	
	E_1	E_2	Additive genetic (h^2_n) ± s.e.	$X^2_{(1)}$	p
3 months	27	50	23 ± 14	5.07	0.02
6 months	20	56	23 ± 11	5.19	0.02
9 months	27	23	50 ± 19	3.62	0.06
12 months	27	43	30 ± 15	4.88	0.03
18 months	15	41	44 ± 11	2.06	0.15
24 months	17	56	27 ± 10	2.37	0.12
30 months	15	42	44 ± 12	2.91	0.09
3 years	11	64	25 ± 7	2.98	0.08
4 years	17	67	16 ± 9	0.26	0.61
5 years	16	44	40 ± 11	1.31	0.25
6 years	12	31	56 ± 12	3.84	0.05

Next in the early years, the largest source of systematic variation is what we would on the simplest assumptions attribute to common environmental factors, E_2. However, the nature of these environmental factors almost certainly changes. Looking at Table VII we see that during the first year of life the gestational age (and its related birth weight) predict mental development. Since gestational age is shared by the twinship, irrespective of zygosity, its effects will contribute to our E_2 and may account for between 14 per cent ($0.37^2 \times 100$) and 34 per cent ($0.58^2 \times 100$) of the total variance in the level of mental development during the first year of life. For older children, this source of age related individual differences is unimportant. Wilson (1978) noted along with Bayley (1965) that the change in the apparent source of environmental variation is associated with the transition from sensorimotor development to the development of symbolic or operational intelligence in Piagetian terms; clearly, as the low correlations of early childhood development with later adult intelligence indicate, we are dealing with different kinds of mental processes whose rate of development is determined by different causal influences.

TABLE VII

Correlation of twins' mental development scores with birth weight, gestational age, socioeconomic status, and mother's education

Age	Birth weight	Gestational age	Socio-economic status	Mother's education
3 months	0.50	0.48	0.04	−0.01
6 months	0.48	0.58	0.08	0.09
12 months	0.30	0.37	0.02	0.09
24 months	0.14	0.12	0.29	0.27
3 years	0.09	0.05	0.35	0.38
6 years	0.18	0.11	0.36	0.33

Note: $n \geqq 350$

Adapted from Wilson (1978). Reprinted by permission from Science, 202, 943. Copyright © 1978 AAAS.

Wilson's reports draw especial attention to the spurts and lags which accompany these developments and he provides sufficient information for us to fit models to the variation in the developmental profile around the overall level. For the later infant period neither environmental nor genetic models seem to account for the data and we must assume that there are either sampling problems or that the psychometric scaling is at fault. For the data up to 30 months using the Bayley Scales and the Stanford-Binet test, divided into first year versus second and third years, the data do conform well but to different models.

In the second and third years of life, we find that the spurts and lags in development are primarily under genetic control with no influence of the family environment (Table VIII). In fact, the arrest and acceleration of intellectual growth during this period would appear to be determined by the genes to an extent at least as great as is the average rate of development.

TABLE VIII

Analysis of variation in the developmental profile during the second and third years of life

Source of variation	d.f.	Mean square	Model E_1	D_R
Between MZ pairs	146	186.2	1	1
Within MZ pairs	148	36.8	1	.
Between DZ pairs	188	204.9	1	¾
Within DZ pairs	190	83.7	1	¼

Parameter estimates

Within family environment: $E_1 = 37.06 \pm 4.11$
Additive genetic effects: $D_R = 188.62 \pm 17.55$
Narrow heritability: $h^2_n = 0.64 \pm 0.13$
Goodness of fit: $X^2_{(2)} = 4.11$ *ns*
All other models fail to fit the observations, $p < 0.05$

During the first year of life again we find that genetic factors predominate, but here we have evidence of the influence of one twin on the other alluded to earlier. In Table IX we have modelled the situation in which an individual's genes may have an effect not only on the individual himself, D_R, but also through him on his twin, D''_R. There will also be a correlation between these effects which will be positive for co-operation and negative for competition. The negative estimate of the covariance, D'_R, between the direct effects of the genes on one's own developmental profile and the indirect effects of these same genes on one's twin indicates competition. Simply put, if I spurt for genetic reasons, my genetically different sibling will if anything be slowed initially. However, recalling that we are discussing spurts and lags around the average developmental rate, this initial lag will be compensated by a subsequent spurt. The data on which this analysis is based are hardly definitive but the interesting questions raised are open to empirical test. In this instance we might predict the developmental instabilities of singleton children to be less marked during the first year of life than those for twins, and especially those for fraternal twins.

TABLE IX

Analysis of variation in the developmental profile during the first year of life

Source of variation	d.f.	Mean square	Model		
			E_1	$(D_R + D''_R)$	D'_R
Between MZ pairs	160	141.4	1	1	2
Within MZ pairs	162	60.6	1	.	.
Between DZ pairs	166	151.7	1	¾	1½
Within DZ pairs	168	112.1	1	¼	-½

Parameter estimates

Within family environment:	$E_1 = 61.49 \pm 6.81$
Directive and indirect (sibling) additive genetic:	$D_R + D''_R = 150.25 \pm 30.81$
Covariance of direct and indirect effects:	$D'_R = -26.10 \pm 13.59$
Goodness of fit:	$X^2_{(1)} = 2.32$ *ns*

All other models fail to fit the observations, $p < 0.05$

The analysis of such effects requires knowledge of the variation for performance both between individuals and within individuals across time. The mere presentation of correlational data is insufficient to answer such questions about this aspect of what might be called the 'genetic environment' (Darlington, 1969; Eaves, et al., 1978).

Whether or not such effects of one individual or another are confirmed for early mental or sensorimotor development, it seems clear that there is evidence of genetic control of spurts and lags in a similar way to that which has been found for instabilities in adult twins' personalities (Eaves and Eysenck, 1976) and childhood weight gains (Wilson, 1979). One might be forgiven for recalling Galton's observation of cases:

> 'where the development of the twins is not strictly *pari passu;* they reach the same goal at the same time, but not by identical stages. Thus: — A is born the larger, then B overtakes and surpasses A, and is in his turn overtaken by A, the end being that the twins become closely alike. This process would aid in giving an interchangeable likeness at certain periods of their growth, and is undoubtedly due to nature more frequently than to nurture'. (Galton 1875).

Maternal Influence and the Twin Family Design

With the analysis of developmental instability and sibling effects, we have considered genetic influences on variation which would otherwise be counted as environmental. Another possibility of this kind arises with twins. It is commonplace to assert that the mother is influential in early childhood cognitive development (Rose *et al.,* 1980). However, children's IQ's are correlated to no greater extent with their mothers than with their fathers (McAskie and Clarke, 1976; Bouchard and McGue, 1981). Thus, *prima facie,* there is little case for considering maternal effects separately from parental influences generally, both of which will contribute to overestimates of the social environmental effects in data from MZ and DZ twins reared together and may account for our high estimate of this source of variation from the Louisville study. However, maternal effects could be of a more complex kind than those which lead simply to an increase in the mother-child correlation and one new approach towards their analysis is through the offspring of identical twins (Nance and Corey, 1976).

FIGURE 3

Variation in offspring data in kinships of MZ twin parents. (From Rose et al., 1980). Reprinted by permission from **Nature**, *24, 376. Copyright © 1980 Macmillan Journals Limited.*

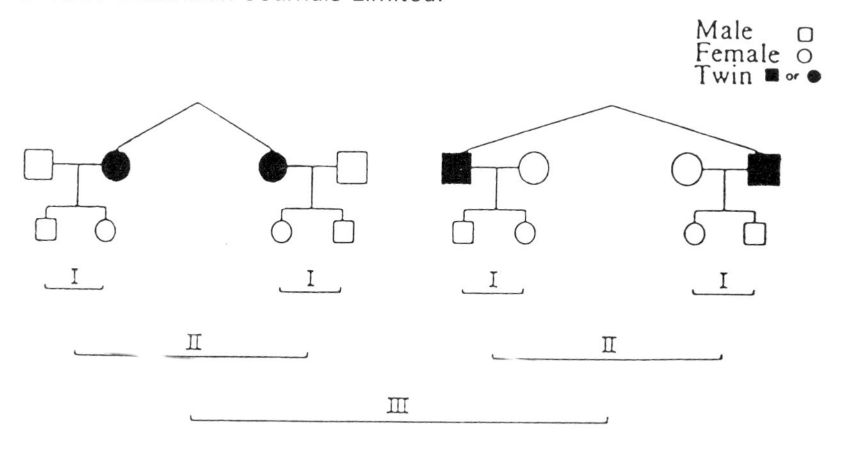

Rose *et al.* (1980) have applied this approach to the verbal subscale of the Wechsler series of intelligence tests. The design of their study can be seen in the pedigrees in Figure 3. The essential features of these pedigrees are, firstly, that offspring of identical twins are related as genetical half-siblings and, secondly, that offspring of identical female twins share genetically the same mother though reared in separate families. Offspring of identical male twins, though equally biologically related, have different mothers. The potential complications of such a situation are considerable as is the potential information to be gained from it. For instance, Hayley, Jinks and Last (1981) showed that by analysing boys' and girls' scores separately from such families we can, in principle, distinguish sex-linkage from maternal effects. However, for our purposes we may simply note that the consequence of genetical or other maternal effects would be that the variation *among* maternal twin-family groups would be inflated while that *between* the families of identical twin mothers would be reduced in comparison to the corresponding statistics for the paternal families.

TABLE X

Analysis of variance for scores on verbal subscales of Wechsler tests for children of MZ twins.

	Subscale			
	Information		Vocabulary	
Source of variation	d.f.	mean square	d.f.	mean square
Among paternal	33	8.56	36	11.12
Between paternal	34	5.53	37	5.69
Among maternal	36	13.13	41	16.03
Between maternal	37	3.66	42	4.77
Within families	194	3.86	240	3.85
F-ratio for maternal effects	1.56 $p < 0.05$		1.37 $p < 0.10$	

Adapted from Rose *et al.* (1980).

Table X summarises Rose *et al's* (1980) analysis and we can see that the data conform to this expected pattern. The effects are not large and though achieving significance for the information subscale are at best of marginal significance for the vocabulary subscale. The ubiquitous problem with attempting to detect relatively small components of variation is that, even with the most sophisticated designs, the overall power of the tests will be low unless the numbers of individuals tested are very large. In fact, for this small data set attempts to fit overall models revealed that those postulating either 100 per cent heritability or 0 per cent heritability could not be unambiguously rejected, although the former was more parsimonious. That human behaviour is not to be understood without effort will come as no surprise. That we have the promise of further refinement in the analysis of another contribution to the 'genetic environment' is at least to be welcomed.

Conclusion

These studies we have reviewed have raised some new questions and, we hope, pointed the way to how we might obtain answers which go beyond the simple estimation of heritability, 'the relative powers of nature and nurture'.

We have seen how maternal effects — the consequences of differential mothering — might be detected and, given the appropriate twin-family designs, these might themselves be analysed in terms of their genetic components. We have seen how the effects of one sibling on another through competition and co-operation are potentially detected and, in the case of very young twins, we found preliminary evidence of genotypic competition. We have seen how spurts and lags in mental development, previously assumed to reflect haphazard vagaries of growth, might themselves be under genetic control.

We have also found that twins in general are more similar to each other than we would predict on the basis of other relatives such as ordinary siblings. This is not the same effect as the often proposed, and repeatedly disproved (Matheny, 1979), hypothesis that the greater similarity of treatment of identical twins compared to fraternal twins will lead to a correspondingly greater similarity in identical twin intelligence, with a consequent overestimation of genetic effects. On the contrary, the actual observed effect might in a simple comparison of MZ and DZ twins lead to an overestimation of the importance of the family environment.

What is the nature of this special twin effect? One possibility is that the greater similarity of treatment of twins in general is indeed responsible. A more prosaic possibility noted by Bouchard and McGue (1981) is that there is a bias towards greater similarity in the recruitment of DZ, and presumably, MZ twins. The third interpretation follows from twins sharing the same age (gestational and chronological), and usually being tested on the same test and probably the same items within the test at the same time. Sources of variance which would usually contribute to unreliability of measurement and reduce the correlation between individuals of different ages would, in the case of twins, contribute to within-pair similarity. Which of these hypotheses — or others in terms of the prenatal or postnatal environment, co-operation effects or secular changes over time — in fact accounts for up to 13 per cent of the variation in their measured intelligence remains to be established.

But all these questions have to be seen in the context of our most plausible model for the data on similarity in collateral relatives. Here, it will be recalled, we estimated the simple broad heritability to be closer to 45 per cent than to the 70-80 per cent from earlier analyses (e.g. Jinks and Fulker, 1970; Jinks and Eaves, 1974). This is in line with that found by other recent reviewers (Plomin and DeFries, 1980). However, we also conclude, along with the earlier analyses, that it is likely that both assortative mating and genetic dominance variation are affecting intelligence, and our best estimate of the level of dominance at individual loci is that it is close to complete.

These broad conclusions were based on weighted least squares modelling of correlations, not corrected for unreliability of measurement which contributes to E_1, from the available data on collateral relatives. It has to be said that inclusion of data from intergenerational pairings (parents and offspring for example) might lead to a less clear picture. But as has been noted by Bouchard and McGue (1981) this will be in part due to the use of different tests for adults and children (McAskie and Clarke, 1976) and in any case is a finding common to the analysis of such measurements as height and finger print ridge count. Further, with data available in the form of correlations alone we are unable to test some assumptions inherent in a simple genetic and environmental model and we are not able to proceed to more informative partitions of the 'genetic environment' (Eaves et al, 1978).

Lastly, although it should not have to be said, in the context of wider debates or other contributions to the discussion of genetics and intelligence, we must restate that none of these results have any bearing on, or lead to any predictions about, the causes of differences between different cultural groups. Those seeking an informed discussion of results which do should read the original papers by Sandra Scarr and her colleagues which, together with critical commentaries, have been reprinted in Scarr (1981).

We might conclude with a final quotation from Sir Francis Galton:

> 'Many a person has amused himself with throwing bits of stick into a tiny brook and watching their progress; how they are arrested, first by one chance obstacle, then by another; and again, how their onward course is facilitated by a combination of circumstances. He might ascribe much importance to each of these events, and think how largely the destiny of the stick has been governed by a series of trifling accidents. Nevertheless, all the sticks succeed in passing down the current, and they travel, in the long run, at nearly the same rate. So it is with life, in respect to the several accidents which seem to have had a great effect upon our careers. The one element, which

varies in different individuals, but is constant in each of them, is the natural tendency; it corresponds to the current in the stream and inevitably asserts itself'. (Galton, 1875).

However, for all his perceptiveness, the data for human intelligence, such as they are, suggest that nature is somewhat less unswerving in its course than Galton's poetic vision would have had it.

References

Bayley, N. (1965). Comparisons of mental and motor test scores for ages 1-15 months by sex, birth order, race, geographical location and education of parents. *Child Development,* 36, 370-411.

Bouchard, T.J. and McGue, M. (1981). Familial studies of intelligence: a review. *Science,* 212, 1055-1059.

Darlington, C.D. (1969). *Evolution of Man and Society.* London: Allen & Unwin.

Eaves, L.J. (1976). A model for sibling effects in man. Heredity, 36, 202-215.

Eaves, L.J., and Eysenck, H.J. (1976). Genetical and environmental components of inconsistency and unrepeatability in twins' responses to a neuroticism questionnaire. *Behavior Genetics,* 6, 359-362.

Eaves, L.J., Last, K.A., Young, P.A. and Martin, N.G. (1978). Model-fitting approaches to the analysis of human behaviour. *Heredity,* 41, 249-320.

Galton, F. (1875). The history of twins as a criterion of the relative powers of nature and nurture. *Fraser's Magazine,* 12, 566-576.

Haley, C.S., Jinks, J.L., and Last, K. (1981). The monozygotic twin half-sib method for analysing maternal effects and sex-linkage in humans. *Heredity,* 46, 227-238.

Jinks, J.L. and Eaves, L.J. (1974). IQ and inequality. *Nature,* 248, 287-289.

Jinks, J.L. and Fulker, D.W. (1970). Comparison of the biometrical genetical, MAVA and classical approaches to the analysis of human behavior. *Psychological Bulletin,* 73, 311-349.

McAskie, M. and Clarke, A.M. (1976). Parent offspring resemblance in intelligence. Theories and evidence. *British Journal of Psychology, 67, 243-273.*

Matheny, A.P. (1979). Appraisal of parental bias in twin studies: ascribed zygosity and IQ differences in twins. *Acta Geneticae Medicae Gemellologiae,* 28, 155-160.

Mather, K. and Jinks, J.L. (1982). *Biometrical Genetics,* Third Edition. London: Chapman and Hall.

Nance, W.E. and Corey, L.A. (1976). Genetic models for the analysis of data from families of identical twins. *Genetics,* 83, 811-826.

Plomin, R. and DeFries, J.C. (1980). Genetics and intelligence: recent data. *Intelligence,* 4, 15-24.

Rose, R.J., Boughman, J.A., Corey, L., Nance, W., Christian, J.C. and Kang, K.W. (1980). Data from kinships of monozygotic twins indicate maternal effects on verbal intelligence. *Nature,* 283, 375-377.

Scarr, S. (1981). *Race, Social Class, and Individual Differences in I.Q.* Hillsdale: Lawrence Erlbaum.

Wilson, R.S. (1977). Mental development in twins. In *Genetics, Environment and Intelligence,* edited by A. Olivero. Amsterdam: North-Holland.

Wilson, R.S. (1978). Synchronies in mental development: an epigenetic perspective. *Science,* 202, 939-948.

Wilson, R.S. (1979). Analysis of longitudinal twin data: basic model and applications to physical growth measures. *Acta Geneticae Medicae Gemellologiae,* 28, 93-105.

The Genetics of Reading Disability

JIM STEVENSON
*Department of Psychology, University of Surrey
Guildford, Surrey.*

PHILIP GRAHAM, GLENDA FREDMAN and
VIVIENNE McLOUGHLIN
*Department of Child Psychiatry, Institute of Child Health,
Hospital for Sick Children, Great Ormond Street, London.*

Within developmental psychology there has been a resurgence of interest in the role of genetic influences on individual differences between children. There are a number of reasons that underlie this change since the time of maximum scepticism about genetically oriented research exemplified by the controversy over Jensen's (1969) paper, Kamin's (1974) attack on the evidence for genetic influences on IQ and the discovery of the inadequacies in Burt's data (Hearnshaw, 1979). The reasons for this change include the continuing limitations found in trying to explain the variance in IQ on the basis of social influences alone (e.g. Yeates *et al.,* 1983), the recognition of possible temperamental and other genetically influenced vulnerabilities to adverse experiences (Rutter, 1981), and the longitudinal twin studies demonstrating genetic control over developmental changes in children (Wilson, 1983). Methodological and theoretical developments have produced models for evaluating genetic influences that recognise the potential complexity of their relationships with environmental factors (Jinks and Fulker, 1970; Scarr and McCartney, 1983) and which have therefore captured the interest of a broader range of psychologists. Finally the move away from reliance on IQ measures as the only phenotypic characteristic intensively investigated has again increased the interests of developmental psychologists. For such psychologists the IQ measure is a singularly barren subject for study since, by definition, *developmental* changes (i.e. changes with age) are eradicated by standardisation. Characteristics that are developmentally more interesting that have been the subject of genetic studies include language development (Hardy-Brown *et al.,* 1981; Ludlow and Cooper, 1983), autism (Folstein and Rutter, 1977) and reading ability (Pennington and Smith, 1983). It is on this latter ability that this paper will concentrate.

We will try to show the way in which the problem of genetic influences on reading ability and disability has been approached in the past and then will illustrate some changes that are necessary in the conceptualisation of these influences as a consequence of a study we have undertaken on reading and other abilities in 13-year old twins. A more detailed account of this study is given in Graham, Stevenson, Fredman and McLoughlin (1984) and Stevenson, Fredman, McLoughlin and Graham (1984a).

Genetics and Reading Disability

In studies on genetic influences on individual differences in cognitive ability, general intelligence has been dominant. However there has always been a theoretical and empirical concern with reading and reading disability running alongside. Indeed from the beginning of the scientific study of reading disability (Hinshelwood, 1907), which was almost contemporaneous with Binet's work on the measurement of IQ, it has been recognised that at least some forms of severe reading disability are familial and moreover assumed to be genetically determined. However, these speculations about some reading handicaps being under hereditary control have been considered contentious, both in terms of the evidence on which they were based and also because of their possible implications for the provision of remedial schooling for children with reading problems. This argument has been encapsulated in a number of statements from leading authorities in the field, e.g. Critchley and Critchley, (1978); Department of Education and Science, (1972); Rutter and Yule, (1975). It should be recognised that the controversy does not just relate to the presence or absence of genetic influences. It is more centrally concerned with the following questions. If a group of children have a qualitatively different problem with reading (a dyslexic group), compared to other children reading less well than might be expected given their general intelligence (specific reading retarded), how are these dyslexics to be recognised? If accurate ascertainment is possible, are their remedial needs any different? The question of genetic influences is bound up with the distinction between 'dyslexia' and specific reading retardation. The full definition of dyslexia produced by Critchley and Critchley (1976) is as follows:

> 'Developmental dyslexia is a learning disability which initially shows itself by difficulty in learning to read and later by erratic spelling and by a lack of facility in manipulating written as opposed to spoken words. The condition is cognitive in essence and usually genetically determined. It is not due to intellectual inadequacy or lack of socio-cultural opportunity or to emotional factors or to any known structural brain deficit. It probably represents a specific maturational defect which tends to lessen as the child grows older

and is capable of considerable improvement, especially when appropriate remedial help is afforded at the earliest opportunity.'

There are three features of this definition that need to be highlighted. Firstly, its use in both clinical and research applications is hampered by its being a definition by exclusion using imprecise criteria, e.g. what is meant by 'lack of socio-cultural opportunity'. Secondly, it includes a recognition that the condition shows itself in different ways as the child develops. Finally there is a specific suggestion of genetic causation.

The evidence available to support this conclusion that dyslexia is genetically determined is weak, surprisingly so given the long-standing suggestion of it being familial. Family studies and segregation analyses can provide evidence consistent with certain modes of inheritance. However, the most direct indication of genetic causation is provided by twin and adoption studies. There have been no published studies concerning reading problems in the adoptive and biological relatives of adopted probands. This leaves the twin studies until recently as the main evidence for genetic factors in reading disability. The linkage study by Smith *et al.*, (1983) has provided a powerful demonstration that one type of reading disability might be due to an autosomal gene on chromosome 15. However, as yet the characteristics of these cases are not well understood and the sample studied is small. What then is the evidence from previous twin studies of genetic influences on reading ability?

Twin Studies on Reading Disability

There are a number of early reports based on Scandinavian samples of twins (Hallgren, 1950; Herman, 1956, 1959; Norrie, 1939, 1954). It is not possible from the accounts of these reports to establish to what extent the samples represent truly independent samples or whether earlier cases are accumulated into the later papers. The percentage concordance rates in monozygotic (identical) pairs was given as 100 per cent and in dizygotic (fraternal) pairs as 33 per cent. In a review of published studies Zerbin-Rudin (1967) found 17 cases of monozygotic (MZ) pairs with at least one twin with a reading difficulty, and 34 similar pairs of dizygotic (DZ) twins. The pairwise concordance rates were 100 per cent and 35 per cent respectively. Bakwin (1973) searched retrospectively for twin pairs referred to his private practice. He located 31 MZ and 31 DZ pairs where again one member of the pair had difficulties with reading. In his study the MZ concordance rate fell below 100 per cent (it was 83 per cent) and the DZ rate remained much lower (29 per cent). The final study is described only scantily by Herschel (1978). He presents findings by Weinschenk (1965) of concordance rates of 100 per cent in MZ and 40 per cent in DZ pairs, but without details of sample size or how the twins were identified.

It can be seen that these twin studies provide data consistent with a strong genetic influence on reading problems in children from a wide range of ages. However, none of those studies is based upon surveys of twins in the general population. Importantly they also lack an adequate operational definition of what constitutes a reading problem. All too often they rely on clinical judgement or teacher reports on whether a problem is present and it is not clear in most cases whether such judgements were made with knowledge of the status of the co-twin's reading.

A Study of a Representative Sample of Twins

It was because of such inadequacies in previous twin studies in this area that the work to be described was undertaken. A total sample of 285 pairs of 13 year old twins were tested in the course of the study. They were recruited from two sources, which we hoped would reduce the possibilities of selection bias. One group had been identified from birth records in a number of London boroughs. These twins had been the subjects in an earlier study by Dr. Anthony Costello. The second group of twins were obtained via schools in the ILEA area. The head teachers in those schools approached the parents on our behalf to ask them to co-operate in the study. A third of the parents refused permission for their twins to take part and this must detract from the overall representativeness of the sample of twins eventually studied.

The twins were all assessed at home by two testers who were blind as to the twins' zygosity or to the co-twin's test performance (since both twins were tested at the same time). The zygosity of the twins was determined both from a variety of biological markers (including blood group testing and dermatoglyphics) and also on the basis of physical similarity using a technique known to be 90 to 95 per cent accurate when compared to blood grouping (Lochlin and Nichols 1976). For full details of zygosity ascertainment and other aspects of methods see Stevenson *et al.,* (1984a). The results of this twin study were such that doubt is cast upon the findings summarised above from earlier investigations of twins. Before discussing these unexpected results concerning reading, we will present some findings on IQ scores in twins that are in agreement with previous research. These establish that our sample of twins are not incapable of replicating the results of other studies!

The twins received IQ assessments using the WISC-R test. In Table I the intraclass correlations for IQ in MZ pairs and the same sex DZ pairs are presented. These correlations are extremely close to the estimates obtained by Plomin and DeFries (1980) from their review of the most satisfactory recent studies on the heritability of IQ. It can be seen that the heritability estimates based on the present study and the Plomin and DeFries survey are lower than those previously reported by Fulker and Eysenck (1979). This is due to the increased value for the DZ correlations in these latest studies. It should be noted that Plomin and DeFries but not Fulker and Eysenck excluded the data on twins reported by Burt.

Like most previous studies (Owen *et al.,* 1971; Finucci *et al.,* 1976) our twins and their families showed strong familiality for reading problems. Table II presents the percentage of different types of relative of twins that were reported to have or had had reading problems. This information is based upon parent reports of problems that created continuing difficulty in education or that were given specific remedial help.

TABLE I

Intraclass correlations for twins and estimates of broad heritability for IQ

	Intraclass correlations		Heritability
	Same sex DZ pairs	*MZ pairs*	h^2
	r_{DZ}	r_{MZ}	$2(r_{MZ}-r_{DZ})$
Fulker and Eysenck (1979)	0.53	0.87	68%
Plomin and DeFries (1980)	0.62	0.86	48%
Present study	0.61	0.84	46%

TABLE II

Incidence of reading problems in the relatives of twins with or without reading problems

	Percentage of relatives with a reading problem	
Relatives	Families of twin without a reading problem n = 195	Families of twin with a reading problem n = 173
Full siblings	6%	15%
Parents	4%	18%
Aunts and Uncles	4%	5%
Cousins	2%	3%

Such data which is not based upon individual assessment is bound to be somewhat inaccurate and subject to biased recall. However it again provided a point of contact between the results of the present study and previous work.

Of course familiality is only a necessary but not sufficient condition to indicate the role of genetic influences. In order to investigate these for reading we have to return to comparisons within twin pairs. The same measures of within pair similarity that were given for IQ can be calculated for reading. These intraclass correlations provide measures of association between the twins' scores across the entire range of reading ability (Table III) i.e. they provide an insight into genetic influences on individual differences in reading *ability* rather than disability. The twins' reading ability was assessed on two measures; one using single word reading (Schonell) and the other based upon the reading of continuous prose (Neale). It can be seen in Table III that both these tests provide estimates for broad heritability that are less than half the value obtained for IQ. By contrast a measure of the twins' spelling ability gave a heritability coefficient of 54 per cent.

TABLE III

Intraclass correlations and heritability estimates for reading and spelling ability

	Intraclass correlations		Heritability
	Same sex DZ pairs $n = 107$	MZ pairs $n = 97$	h^2
	r_{DZ}	r_{MZ}	$2(r_{MZ} - r_{DZ})$
Neale Reading Age	0.52	0.61	18%
Schonell Reading Age	0.51	0.61	20%
Schonell Spelling Age	0.49	0.76	54%

It is well established that reading ability is correlated with IQ and it is possible that the heritabilities given in Table III are simply due to genetic influences on IQ i.e. there are not separate effects of genetic factors on reading. It is necessary therefore to obtain a measure of reading ability for each child that is independent of IQ. This can be achieved by the use of multiple regression procedures. The regression equations were estimated for each reading and spelling score separately on IQ and age. The subsequent calculation of residual scores for each child provides an indication of how well the child is reading compared to what would be expected given the child's general ability; these measures will be called IQ adjusted reading ages. Table IV summarises the heritabilities of these IQ adjusted scores, which remain about the same as in Table III for reading but are increased for spelling. These results establish that for the full range of ability there are genetic factors acting to influence individual differences in reading, but more especially in spelling, that have effects that are independent of those acting on general ability as measured by IQ.

TABLE IV

Intraclass correlations and heritability estimates for IQ adjusted reading and spelling ages

	Intraclass correlations		Heritability
	Same sex DZ pairs $n = 107$	MZ pairs $n = 97$	h^2 $\frac{(r_{MZ} - r_{MZ})}{2(r_{MZ} - r_{DZ})}$
	r_{DZ}	r_{MZ}	
IQ adjusted Neale Reading Age	0.42	0.51	18%
IQ adjusted Schonell Reading Age	0.37	0.51	28%
IQ adjusted Schonell Spelling Age	0.39	0.75	72%

These conclusions based on analysis of data from all the twins studied do not necessarily apply to the causation of reading disability. In the case of general intelligence it is well established that the influences on low IQ are somewhat different from those operating on individual differences in the normal range. In addition to the environmental and polygenic influences acting on all members of the population a number of major single genes (e.g. those producing PKU), non-heritable genetic influences (e.g. chromosomal aberrations) and experiential factors during maturation (e.g. anoxia) are responsible for producing low IQs. In reading it is possible therefore that, although genetic effects are operating on all children. marked underachievement in reading is entirely due to the influences of severe maturational or experiential events and therefore not heritable.

The findings from this study relevant to this question are presented in Table V. The summary statistics in this table are in the form of pairwise concordance rates which are the number of pairs in which both twins show a condition expressed as a percentage of all pairs continuing at least one twin with this condition. Disability has been defined in a number of ways in Table V, however in each case the definition indicates a degree of handicap whereby a child is 18 months or more behind its peers. Reading backwardness is defined as a Schonell Reading Age 18 months or more below the mean for this group of twins. Specific reading retardation is present when the child's Schonell Reading Age is more than 18 months below that expected given its IQ and chronological age. Spelling backwardness and specific spelling retarda tion are defined in an analogous manner but based upon the Schonell Spelling Age. An operational definition of 'dyslexia' that is often used in studies on reading is that the child should be reading backward (in the sense given above) but with an IQ that is within the normal range i.e. greater than 90. This definition has many weaknesses but is used here to provide comparability with some previous studies.

TABLE V

Concordance rates for reading and spelling disabilities

	Pairwise concordance rates Same sex	
Disability	DZ n = 107	MZ n = 97
Reading backward (Schonell)	27%	33%
Specific reading retarded (Schonell)	18%	21%
'Dyslexia'	17%	33%
Spelling backward	25%	42%
Specific spelling retarded	20%	33%

The first striking feature of the concordance rates presented in Table V is that all the MZ concordances are very much below the almost perfect concordances reported in earlier twin studies. Indeed for reading backwardness and specific reading retardation they are only slightly greater than the DZ concordances. Both the spelling disabilities and 'dyslexia' show more consistent MZ/DZ differences. It may be considered that 18 months is an arbitary cut-off point for delineating disability and that a difficult result might have been obtained using a more marked degree of disability. When concordance rates are compared using increasing degrees of disability (24, 30, 36 months behind) only specific spelling retardation maintains a consistently higher MZ than DZ concordance rate. These data then indicate that for reading disability there seems to be rather little contribution of genetic influences but that for specific difficulties with spelling genetic factors may well be present. However even for spelling where the indicators of genetic effects are greatest the concordance rates are nowhere near as high for identical twins as previous studies have claimed. It is necessary then to compare carefully our study with the earlier reports on twins to establish any methodological differences that might account for this disagreement in the findings over the role of genetic factors in the causation of reading disability.

The first clear distinction between this and previous studies was our attempt to identify systematically a sample of twins that would be representative of the general population. As described above, Hallgren, Norrie and Hermann relied upon twins with reading problems being known to the education services without routine assessments on all twins. Zerbin-Rudin (1967) collated isolated case reports appearing in the literature. The representativeness of such cases is unknown though it might be surmised that concordant identical twins may be thought by clinicians to be of greater 'interest' than discordant pairs and accordingly more likely to be reported in the literature. Bakwin (1973) obtained his twins from referrals to his private practice: it might again be suggested that twins are more likely to receive such a referral if both suffer from a particular condition. It can be argued then that each of these different sampling procedures will lead to inflated concordances especially in identical twins.

Secondly, by conducting identical assessments of the reading abilities of all the twins in the sample it was possible to utilise exactly equivalent operational definitions of the different types of disability. For example it is not clear whether other disabilities such as language delay might have been included in the reading problem diagnosis adopted by Hallgren (1950). It is possible that such contamination of assessment took place with other of the earlier studies also.

The third possible methodological difference lies in the designation of zygosity. In the present study zygosity assessment was based either on earlier biological indicators or through physical similarity ratings. In both methods the zygosity designation was completely independent of information concerning the twins' reading ability. It is not clear from accounts of previous studies whether twins known to be concordant for reading or other educationally related disability were more likely to be identified as MZ, and hence create circularity in the twin method by contaminating the zygosity assessment with similarity in the dependent variable.

A fourth possibility is that by providing a more stringent method for controlling for general intelligence, genetic effects have tended to disappear. Previous studies tended either to ignore the problem of differentiating specific from general disability or did so by requiring normal IQ before designating a particular child as showing a reading problem. An indication that this difference was in fact having an effect on the results can be seen in the concordance rates for 'dyslexia' in Table V. This condition is similar to that used in previous investigations and did provide greater MZ/DZ differences in concordance rates than specific reading retardation defined on the basis of regression equations that were not available to the earlier studies.

Blind assessment of the twins was a fifth methodological development adopted in this study. The two testers obtained the reading and other measures simultaneously. This precluded the possibility of knowledge of one twin's reading ability influencing the identification of a reading problem in the co-twin. It is very likely that such biasing of assessment takes place when reliance is placed on clinical judgement of the presence of reading problems. The direction of such biases might be in the direction of highlighting contrasts between members of the same twin pair or might be such as to inflate measures of similarity artificially.

These five methodological inadequacies in the design of the earlier studies may have contributed to their identification of artificially inflated concordance rates in MZ twins. There is one further feature of the present study that might have mitigated against the identificatiion of strong genetic effect on reading. All the twins were tested during a restricted age range around their thirteenth birthdays. It is possible that children with an initial difficulty with reading might have overcome this problem by the age of thirteen. The definition of dyslexia given above from Critchley and Critchley (1978) specifically suggests that early reading problems may be seen later only as a residual problem with spelling. It was with spelling that all the analyses undertaken with these 13-year old twins showed the strongest genetic influences. It is possible therefore if these same twins had been studied at a younger age that reading too would have shown genetic effects. However by the age of 13 a number of twins, not necessarily from the same twin pairs, may have overcome their initial reading problems. The concordance rates for reading at 13 are then observed to be lower than for spelling disability at the same age, whereas they would have been high for both disabilities at a younger age.

This argument leads to the conclusion that genetic influences on literacy problems are more appropriately studied through their impact on spelling ability. The significance of the dissociation of reading and spelling ability has been emphasised by Frith (1980, 1984). The task of being able to produce the correct written representation of a particular word demands different cognitive skills from those required to generate an appropriate pronounciation of a word. The nature of these processes underlying reading and spelling have been investigated in the present study (Stevenson *et al.,* 1984a, b), and these analyses support the conclusion that individual differences in the skills that are most central to spelling are more strongly influenced by genetic factors than those utilised in reading.

Although the main concern of this paper has been to present conclusions on the genetic influences on reading, the data can also be used to investigate the role of environmental influences on individual differences. Indeed the findings of the twin study indicate that an exploration of factors other than genetic ones should be fruitful at least for reading, if less so for spelling. The results of this aspect of the study can be found in Stevenson *et al.,* (1984c).

A final word of caution needs to be made concerning our understanding of genetics and reading disability. it is clear that literacy is a complex set of interdependent skills. The range of genetic and environmental influences on such a complex ability is likely to be large. It should not be expected that only one genetic mechanism is likely to be operating. As mentioned in the introduction, Smith *et al.,* (1983) have established the role of a dominant allele at a locus on chromosome 15 in producing reading problems. There are likely to be other genetic mechanisms at work. For example, Lewitter, De Fries and Elston (1980) suggest that their segregation analysis of the pedigrees of children with reading problems demonstrates genetic heterogeneity including evidence of a sex limited autosomal recessive gene being responsible for the pattern of incidence seen in the families of female probands. It is certainly inappropriate to attempt to summarise this variety of genetic mechanisms and their interactions with environmental influences in terms of a single heritability coefficient or other population statistic. We require more detailed examinations of genetic and environmental influences on literacy but need to clarify in parallel the complex skills on which reading and spelling are based and the various types of disability that can be produced by failure to acquire these skills.

Acknowledgements

The work reported here was supported by a project grant from the M.R.C. We would like to state our gratitude to the other members of the research team, without whose contribution the work could not have been completed: Kate Bertram, Rachelle Broughton, Becky Dobbs, and Elizabeth Nabarro.

References

Bakwin, H. (1973). Reading disability in twins. *Developmental Medicine and Child Neurology,* 15, 184-187.

Critchley, M. and Critchley, E.A. (1978). *Dyslexia Defined.* London: Heinemann.

Department of Education and Science. (1972). *Children with specific reading difficulties.* Report of the Advisory Committee on Handicapped Children. London: H.M.S.O.

Finucci, J.M., Guthrie, J.T., Childs, A.L., Abbey, H. and Childs, B. (1976). The genetics of specific reading disability. *Annals of Human Genetics,* 40, 1-23.

Folstein, S. and Rutter, M. (1977). Infantile autism: a genetic study of 21 twin pairs. *Journal of Child Psychology and Psychiatry,* 18, 297-321.

Frith, U. (1980). Unexpected spelling problems. In *Cognitive Processes in Spelling,* edited by U. Frith (pp. 495-515). London: Academic Press.

Frith, U. (1984). The similarities and differences between reading and spelling problems. In *Developmental Neuropsychiatry,* edited by M. Rutter, Edinburgh: Churchill Livingstone.

Fulker, D.W. and Eysenck, H.J. (1979). Nature and nurture: heredity. In *The Structure and Measurement of Intelligence,* edited by H.J. Eysenck. Berlin: Springer-Verlag.

Graham, P., Stevenson, J., Fredman, G. and McLoughlin, V. (1985). A twin study of genetic influences on behavioral deviance. *Journal of the American Academy of Child Psychiatry,* (in press).

Hallgren, B. (1950). Specific dyslexia: a clinical and genetic study. *Acta Psychiatrica and Neurologica Scandinavica (Supplement).* 165, 1-287.

Hardy-Brown, K., Plomin, R. and De Fries, J.C. (1981). Genetic and environmental influences on the rate of communicative development in the first year of life. *Developmental Psychology,* 17, 704-717.

Hearnshaw, L.S. (1979). *Cyril Burt, Psychologist.* London: Hodder and Stoughton.

Herman, K. (1956). Congenital word blindness. *Acta Psychiatrica and Neurologica Scandinavica (Supplement),* 103, 1-138.

Hermann, K. (1959). *Reading Disability: a Medical Study of Word Blindness and Related Handicaps.* Copenhagen: Munksgaard.

Herschel, M. (1978). Dyslexia revisited: a review. *Human Genetics,* 40, 115-134.

Hinshelwood, J. (1907). Four cases of congenital word blindness occurring in the same family. *British Medical Journal,* 2, 1229-1232.

Jensen, A.R. (1969). How much can we boost IQ and scholastic achievement. *Harvard Educational Review,* 39, 1-123.

Jinks, J.L. and Fulker, D.W. (1970). A comparison of biometrical genetical, MAVA and classical approaches to the analysis of human behavior. *Psychological Bulletin,* 73, 311-349.

Kamin, L. (1974). *The Science and Politics of IQ.* Potomac, Maryland: Lawrence Erlbaum Associates.

Lewitter, F.I., De Fries, J.C. and Elston, R.C. (1980). Genetic models of reading disability. *Behaviour Genetics,* 10, 9-30.

Loehlin, J.C. and Nichols, R.C. (1976). *Heredity, environment and personality: a study of 850 sets of twins.* Austin: University of Texas Press.

Ludlow, C.L. and Cooper, J.A. (Eds.) (1983). *Genetic Aspects of Speech and Language Disorders.* New York; Academic Press.

Norrie, E. (1939). *Om Ordblinhet.* Copenhagen: Munksgaard.

Norrie, E. (1954). Ordblinhedens (dyslexiens) arvegang. *Laesepaedagogen,* 2, 61.

Owen, F., Adams, P., Forrest, T., Stolz, L. and Fisher, S. (1971). Learning disorders in children; sibling studies. *Monographs of the Society for Research in Child Development.* 36, 1-74.

Pennington, B.F. and Smith, S.D. (1983). Genetic influences on learning disabilities and speech and language disorders. *Child Development,* 54, 369-387.

Plomin, R. and De Fries, J.C. (1980). Genetics and intelligence: recent data. *Intelligence,* 4, 15-24.

Rutter, M. (1981). Stress, coping and development: some issues and some questions. *Journal of Child Psychology and Psychiatry,* 22, 323-356.

Rutter, M. and Yule, W. (1975). The concept of specific reading retardation. *Journal of Child Psychology and Psychiatry,* 16, 181-197.

Scarr, S. and McCartney, K. (1983). How people make their own environments: a theory of genotype — environment effects. *Child Development,* 54, 424-435.

Smith, S.D., Kimberling, W.J., Pennington, B.F. and Lubs, H.A. (1983). Specific reading disability: identification of an inherited form through linkage analysis. *Science,* 219, 1245-1347.

Stevenson, J., Graham, P., Fredman, G. and McLoughlin, V. (1984a). *A twin study of genetic influences on reading ability and disability.* (submitted for publication).

Stevenson, J., Fredman, G., McLoughlin, V. and Graham, P. (1984b). *An exploration of genetic influences on the two-route model of reading.* (submitted for publication).

Stevenson, J., Fredman, G., McLoughlin, V. and Graham, P. (1984c). *Environmental influences on reading ability.* (submitted for publication).

Weinschenk, C. (1965). *Die erbliche Rechtschreibschwache und ihre socialpsychiatrischen Auswirkungen.* Bern: Huber.

Wilson, R.S. (1983). The Louisville Twin Study: developmental synchronies in behavior. *Child Development,* 54, 298-316.

Yeates, K.O., MacPhee, D., Campbell, F.A. and Ramey, C.T. (1983). Maternal IQ. and home environment as determinants of early childhood intellectual competence: a developmental analysis. *Developmental Psychology,* 19, 731-739.

Zerbin-Rudin, E. (1967). Congenital word blindness. *Bulletin of the Orton Society,* 17, 47-54.

Biosocial Correlates of IQ

G.C.N. MASCIE-TAYLOR
Department of Physical Anthropology,
University of Cambridge, Cambridge

The identification of sources of variation in intelligence test scores has been the subject of many investigations as well as theoretical studies (Vernon, 1979; McManus and Mascie-Taylor, 1983). Over the past decade or so these efforts have received a new impetus as a consequence of the revival of the venerable nature-nurture controversy. The results of these and earlier studies indicate that individual differences in IQ can be shown to relate to social and biological variables, personal attributes and to family conditions. In fact most variables studied show some association with IQ score be it social class, family size, birth order, season of birth or even head circumference (Deutch *et al.,* 1968; Plowden, 1967; Anastasi, 1956; Nisbet, 1953; Douglas, 1964; Davie *et al.,* 1972; Rutter, *et al.,* 1970; Douglas *et al.,* 1968; Nisbit and Entwistle, 1967; Belmont and Marolla, 1973; Mascie-Taylor, 1980b, 1980c; Broman *et al.,* 1975).

Unfortunately there has been a tendency to examine the effect of most variables separately without considering the possible effects or contributions of other variables or their interactions to the resultant association.

For example, numerous investigations have examined the relationship between birth order and IQ score (Kunz and Peterson, 1973; 1977). Although the majority of studies have found that first born have, on average, higher IQs than later born off-spring, this is not always the case (Zajonc, 1976). A number of review articles on birth order and IQ have pointed to the considerable methodological problems as well as the inconsistant results (Jones, 1933; Clausen, 1966; Altus, 1966; Schooler, 1972). Much of this inconsistency stems from the use of highly selected samples and a failure to control for family size and social class, both of which are associated with IQ score variation (Adams, 1972; Wray, 1971). The conclusion to be drawn from this example seem straight forward: (a) examine as many variables as possible and their interactions when seeking to identify sources of variation in IQ test scores, (b) try not to use small selected samples but use, if possible, large random samples.

One study that fulfilled these requirements is that reported by Broman, *et al.,* (1975). They investigated the relationship between IQ at age four and a variety of factors, related to the prenatal period, delivery, neonatal period and the infancy and childhood period. The subjects were 26,760 white and negro American children whose mothers had enrolled during pregnancy in the Collaborative Perinatal Project, a longitudinal study of development in the first eight years of life conducted by the National Institute of Neurological Diseases and Stroke.

Their results can be summarized as follows:—

(1) Of the 169 variables screened, 73 significantly correlated with IQ score in the white population and 59 in the negro population.

(2) The prenatal variables accounted for 20 per cent of the IQ variance within the white group, and 11 per cent among negro girls and 8 per cent among negro boys. The variables making the largest independent contributions to the IQ score at age four were 'education of the mother and socioeconomic index of the family'.

(3) The addition of neonatal variables increased the amount of explained variance by only 1-2 per cent. The neonatal variable making a small independent contribution was physical measurement at birth (head circumference of whites, length of Negro boys and weight of Negro girls).

(4) The infancy and childhood variables increased the amount of variance accounted for by 4-6 per cent. All variables combined accounted for 28 per cent of the variance in IQ among white girls, 25 per cent among white boys, 17 per cent among Negro girls and 15 per cent among Negro boys.

The results obtained from this U.S. study suggest that there is a third requirement besides a large random sample and the examination of the effects of a large number of variables; one also requires longitudinal information about the child or persons studied.

The work described in this paper fulfills all these requirements.

Material

The data set comprises the National Child Development Study (NCDS). This study commenced as the Perinatal Mortality Survey and involved all children born in Britain during the week 3rd-9th March, 1958. At that time detailed obstetric data were collected on each child (Butler and Bonham, 1963; Butler and Alberman, 1969). The surviving children, together with any others in the same birth cohort entering the country after that data were followed up in 1965, again at age 11 (1969), at age 16 (1974) and they have recently been restudied (1983).

The results here are based on psychometric data collected at age 11. Four tests were given at that time: a reading test, a mathematics test and tests of verbal and non-verbal IQ (Fogelman *et al.,* 1978; Adams, *et al.,* 1976). The last two in combination yield a total IQ score. It is the latter measure that has been used in most of the analyses presented in this paper. The IQ test has been standardised with a mean of 100 and standard deviation of 15 IQ points.

This study examined the relationship between IQ and the following variables:—

1. Maternal history of smoking both prior to and during pregnancy.
2. Birth weight.
3. Gestation period.
4. Maternal blood groups: ABO and Rhesus.
5. Mean parental age at the time of the child's birth.
6. Difference in age of the two parents.
7. Sex of the child.
8. Social class of the father when the child was aged 11, classified according to the Registrar General's Classification into 5 categories.
9. Birth order.
10. Family size.
11. Tenure (owner occupied or tied to occupation, private, rented or council).
12. Accommodation (whole house/bungalow versus flat, rooms or caravan).
13. Child receiving free school meals.
14. Crowding status.
15. Number sharing bedroom.
16. Number sharing bed.
17. Basic household amenities.
18. Father unemployed versus employed.
19. Working mother.
20. Financial status.
21. Handedness.
22. Eye dominance.
23. Height.
24. Parental status.
25. Number of school moves.
26. Number of family moves.
27. Social mobility.
28. Geographical mobility.
29. Regional differences.

Results

Social class differences

Numerous studies in both this country and in other parts of the world have shown quite substantial correlations between parental social class and both the IQ and scholastic attainment of their children. (e.g. Davie *et al.,* 1972). Douglas *et al.,* (1968) found for the British National Survey data that middle class children had considerably higher intelligence and attainment scores than did their working class counterparts. Furthermore, several studies have shown that mild mental retardation mainly occurs in families in which the father has an unskilled or semi-skilled manual occupation. Mild retardation is in addition particularly common when there is poverty, family disorganisation, overcrowding and a large number of offspring. In these circumstances it is quite common for several of the children to be mildly retarded or to have an IQ score near the bottom end of the normal range (Rutter and Madge, 1976).

The direct way in which social class influences could be demonstrated is by determining the association between parental social class and the child's IQ within a sample of adopted children in which selective placement has not occurred. Data which approach this ideal are available from some early American studies (Leahy, 1935; Burks, 1928; Skodak and Skeels, 1949). The studies indicated a low association between adoptive father's occupational status and the children's IQ.

Unfortunately the NCDS data set does not lend itself to analysis of this type. However it can be used to give an indirect measure of the effect of social class. From the earlier remarks it is clear that social class is liable to be confounded by other factors such as family income, overcrowding, family size and birth order. It would be of interest, therefore, to see what IQ differences are associated with social class *per se* and what differences remain after removing those effects accounted for by confounding variables.

Such analyses have been undertaken and the results are illustrated in Figure 1. Social class has been subdivided into 5 categories:— I Professional, II Managerial, III Skilled, IV Semi-Skilled, V Unskilled. The IQ score of social class V has been set to zero. The upper line shows the relationship between IQ and social class *per se* (U stands for uncorrected), and the lower line that after removal of the controlling variables (C for corrected).

The statistical significance of social class was found by examining the extra variance contributed by it after the effects of all other controlling variables had been removed. For many of the variables quadratic, cubic and quartic terms were used, the significance of higher order terms being tested only after lower terms for that variable had been fitted. In total 97 main effect terms (variables and their higher order terms) were included in the multiple regression analyses before the contribution of social class was considered. It can readily be seen that even after removing prenatal, natal, biological, family and social factors a large and significant social class/IQ association still remains; the range of mean IQ difference between social classes still exceeds ten IQ points.

All subsequent statistical analyses described in this paper follow the procedure outlined for social class i.e. the significance of a predictor

FIGURE 1
Relationship between IQ of children and parental social class.
The IQ score of social class V has been set to zero. U = uncorrected scores; C = scores after removal of controlling variables.

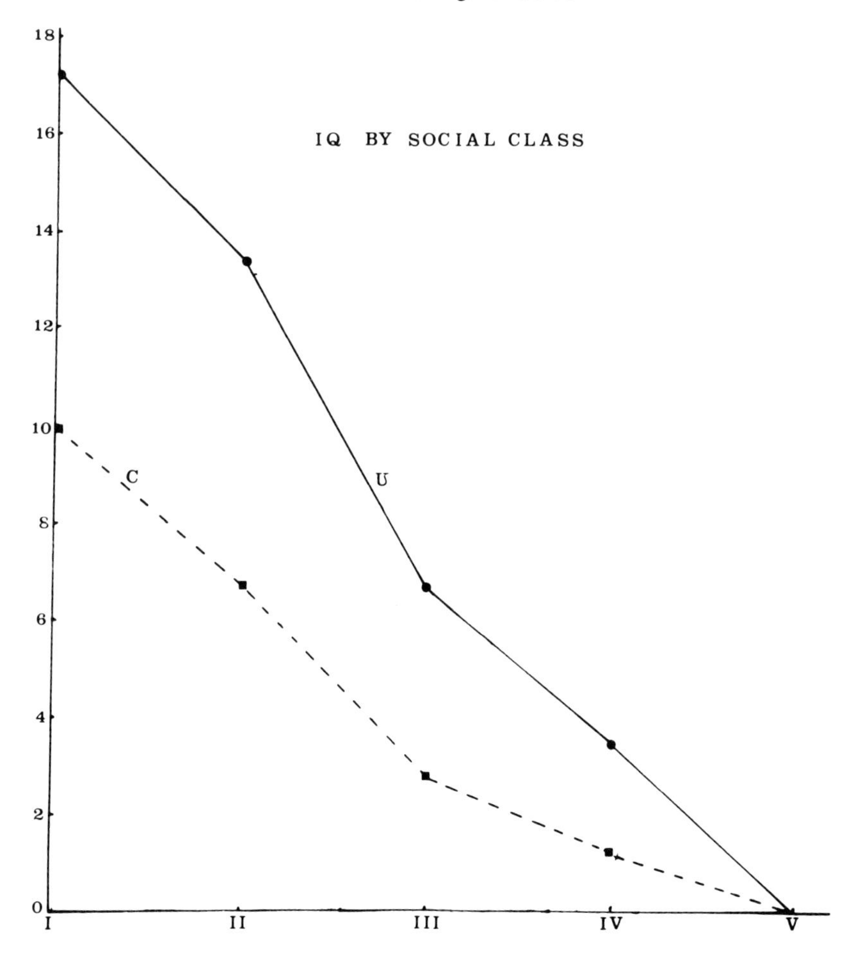

variable was found by examining the extra variance contributed by it after the main effects of all other variables had been removed.

Family size and birth order

The disadvantages of coming from a large family appear to start at birth and continue throughout childhood. (e.g. Fogelman, 1983). The chance of a child being born alive and surviving the first week of life

FIGURE 2
Relationship between IQ of children and family size.
The IQ score at family size 4+ has been set to zero.

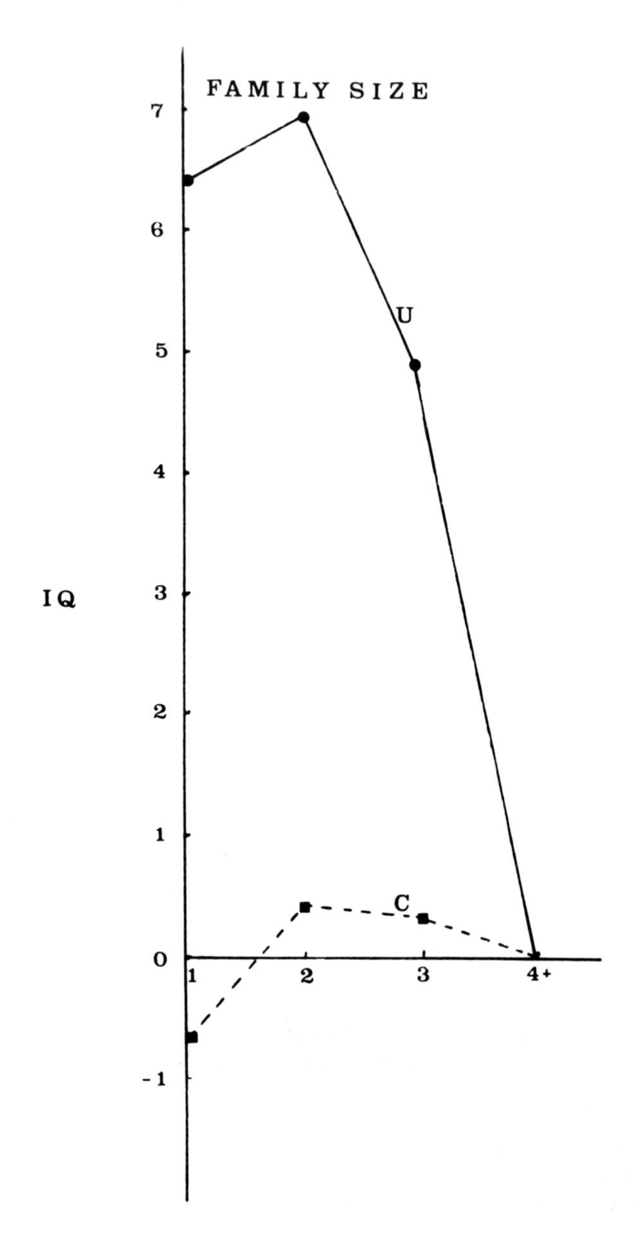

FIGURE 3
Relationship between IQ of children and birth order.
The IQ score at birth order 5+ has been set to zero.

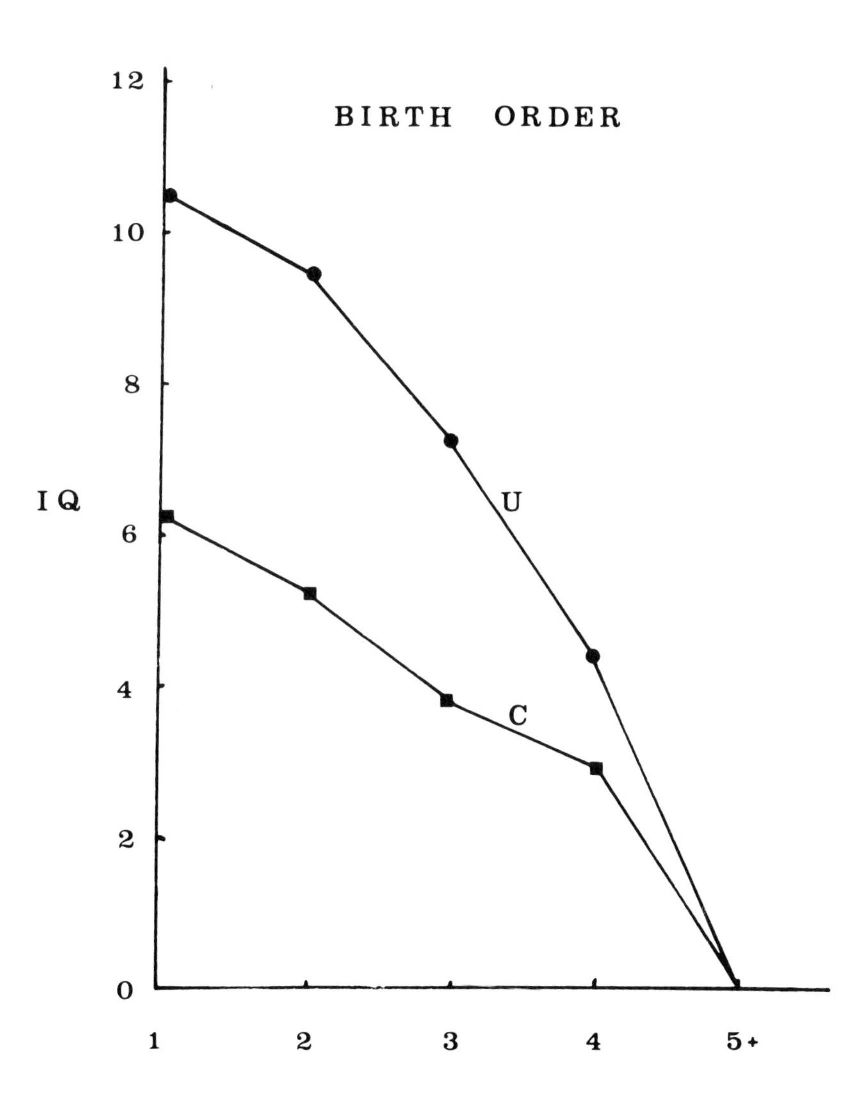

is greater for earlier born than for those children who are fourth or later born. For school age children there is considerable evidence that individuals from large families tend to have a lower level of intelligence and reading attainment than those from smaller families (Lieberman, 1970). The association between large family size and low attainment applies most strongly to verbal intelligence and reading and is much less evident in non-verbal intelligence.

For the NCDS data the relationship between IQ score and family size *per se* is in agreement with earlier published findings (Figure 2). However after removal of the main effects only a small and insignificant association of family size with IQ score remains. This result would suggest that the relationship between family size and IQ score is not so marked and certainly smaller than had previously been suggested (Floud *et al.,* 1956; Dale and Griffith 1965; Davie *et al.,* 1972).

The relationship between birth order and IQ score has already been mentioned in the introduction to this paper. For this data set the range of mean IQ's from first to fifth-plus born exceeded ten IQ points but this dropped to six IQ points after removal of the other main effects (Figure 3). Birth order shows a highly significant association with total IQ score even after the confounding effects, particularly of family size and social class, have been removed.

Maternal blood groups

The study of the relationship between segregating genetic markers and psychometric variables has been strongly advocated by Thoday (1967) as a means of analysing continuous variables in human populations. This approach has already led to the report of an association between IQ score and ABO blood groups in a group of Oxfordshire villages (Gibson *et al.,* 1973) and in Cambridge families (Mascie-Taylor, 1977); between PTC tasting ability and personality and IQ test scores (Mascie-Taylor *et al.,* 1983) and between haptoglobin phenotypes and spatial ability (Mascie-Taylor *et al.,* 1984). Although blood group information was not collected on the children in the sample, there were data on maternal ABO and Rhesus blood groups. It can be seen that the effects are slightly greater for Rhesus than for ABO, although both are quite small (Figure 4).

Smoking in pregnancy, birth weight and gestation period

Smoking in pregnancy has been shown to be associated with lowered birth weight and with an increased risk of perinatal death (Butler and Alberman, 1969). It has also been shown that children born to mothers who smoked in pregnancy are shorter and read less well at age 7 years than do children whose mothers did not smoke, (Davie *et al.,* 1972; Fogelman, 1980). The results for this study indicate that one can

FIGURE 4
Deviations of children's IQ scores from the mean in relation to maternal blood group, and in relation to mothers' smoking before and during pregnancy.

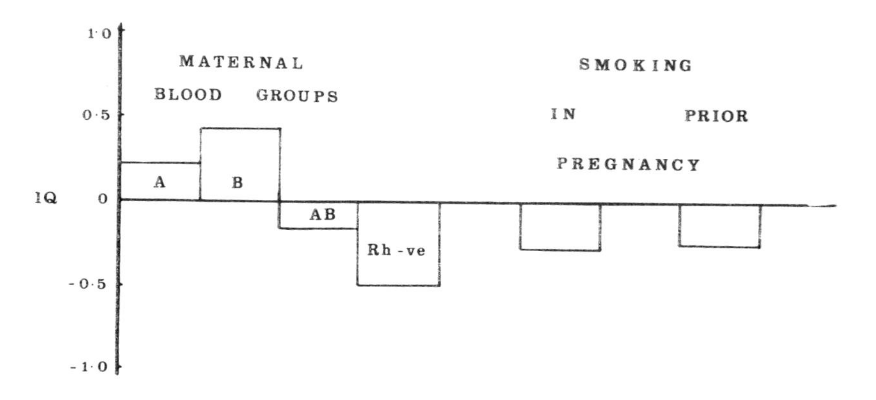

FIGURE 5
Relationship between children's IQ, and birth weight expressed as standard deviations above and below the mean. The IQ score of children of mean birthweight has been set at zero.

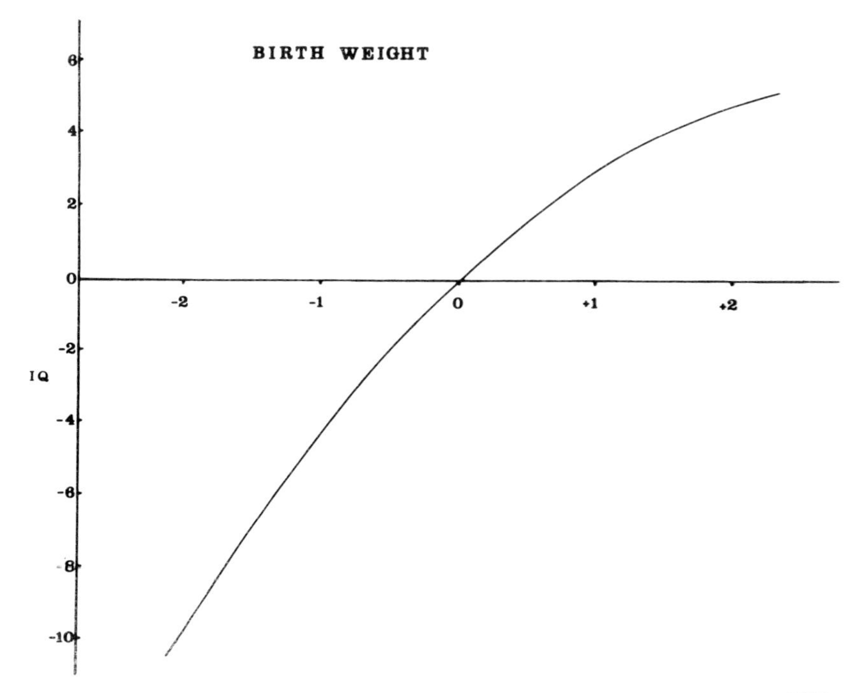

distinguish an association between smoking and IQ score, even if the mother ceased to smoke as soon as she knew she was pregnant (Figure 4).

The association between birth weight and IQ score is quite dramatic. Figure 5 indicates that those below the 95 percentile tend to have an IQ deficit of ten points.

The gestation period association is relatively less marked (Figure 6). However, analyses indicate that low birth weight, short gestation period and smoking in pregnancy each show substantially independent effects since each was tested for significance after removal of all other effects. The IQ deficit of a child at age 11 whose birth weight and gestation period were two standard deviations below the mean and whose mothers smoked in pregnancy exceeds nine IQ points.

Disadvantage

A person's life circumstances are shaped to a considerable extent by the type of house in which he lives. So poor housing, together with low income, is associated with a wide range of personal troubles as well as social disadvantage (Rutter and Madge, 1976).

FIGURE 6
Relationship between period of gestation, expressed as standard deviations either side of the mean, and children's IQ.

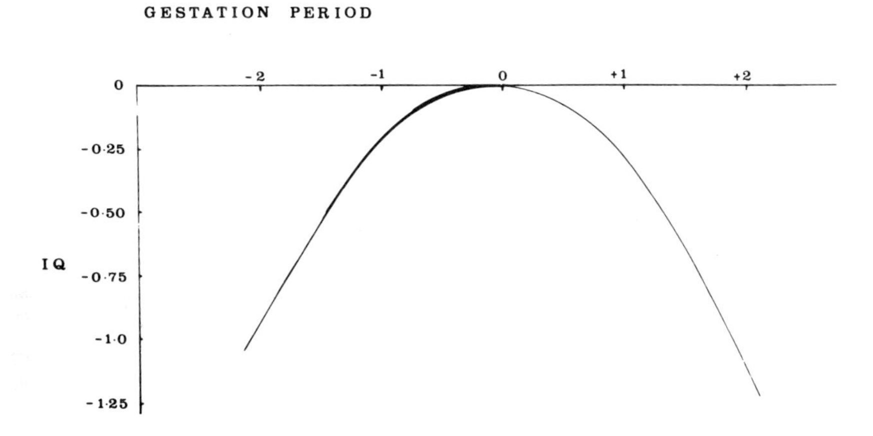

Housing standards are assessed on a number of criteria, such as structural soundness, availability of basic facilities and degree of crowding. Various assessments of overcrowding have been made but in recent years there has been a tendency to use the ratio of persons per room.

Many studies have shown that children living in overcrowded homes tend to have less good educational attainment than other children (Douglas, 1964; Davie *et al.,* 1972; Petzing and Wedge, 1970). As Rutter and Madge (1976) point out, overcrowding may influence school performance through lack of play space, the unavailability of a quiet room to study and perhaps through disturbance of sleep by other family members.

The NCDS data have been used to examine the relationships between these disadvantages and IQ scores. Information was collected on use of household amenities. The amenities comprised· indoor lavatory, bathroom and hot water supply. There were four categories: (1) sole use of all amenities (2) sole use of two (3) sole use of one (4) sole use of no amenity. Of the 13,644 families, 87.7 per cent had sole use of all, 6.3 per cent sole use of two and 3.0 per cent for each of the last two categories. The results are shown in Figure 7. Lack of amenities still shows a statistical effect of over two IQ points between those who have sole use and those who have no use, even after all other main effects have been removed.

FIGURE 7
Relationship between housing conditions and children's IQ. Crowding and amenities expressed in arbitrary units (see text).

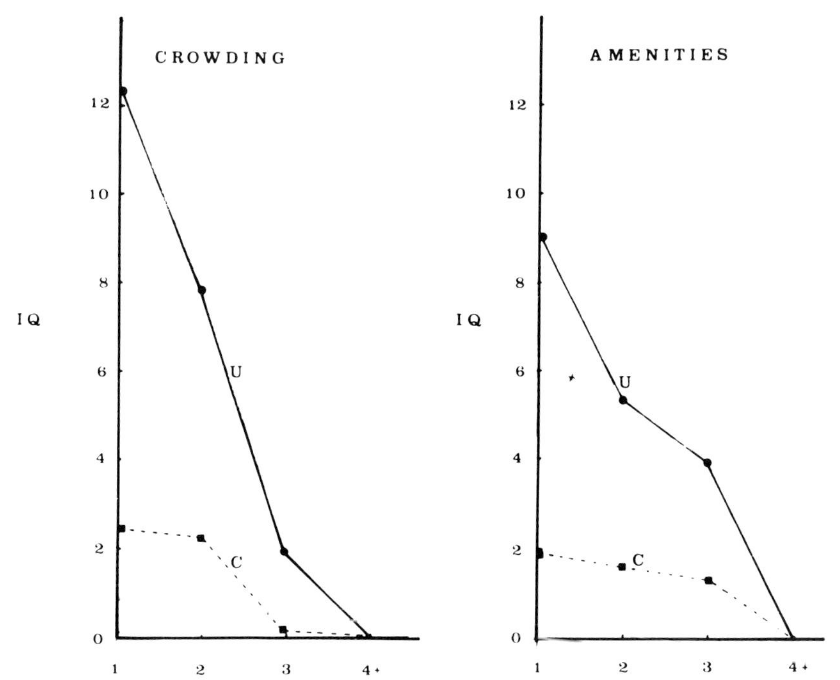

The same figure also illustrates the relationship between crowding and IQ scores. Crowding was qualified as follows:—

1	= up to 1 person/room	60.6%
2	= 1-1.5 persons/room	27.3%
3	= 1.5-2.0 persons/room	9.5%
4	= 2.0 + persons/room	2.6%

The numbers in brackets refer to the percentages in each of these categories (n = 13797). As with the analysis for household amenities there remains a statistical effect of overcrowding.

As has been mentioned, overcrowding may also manifest itself through disturbance of sleep by other family members. As information was also available on bed-sharing and number of people sharing a bedroom, it seemed worthwhile seeing whether or not these two factors showed an independent relationship to IQ score variation. For the NCDS, 17.3

FIGURE 8
Effect of sleeping conditions on children's IQ.

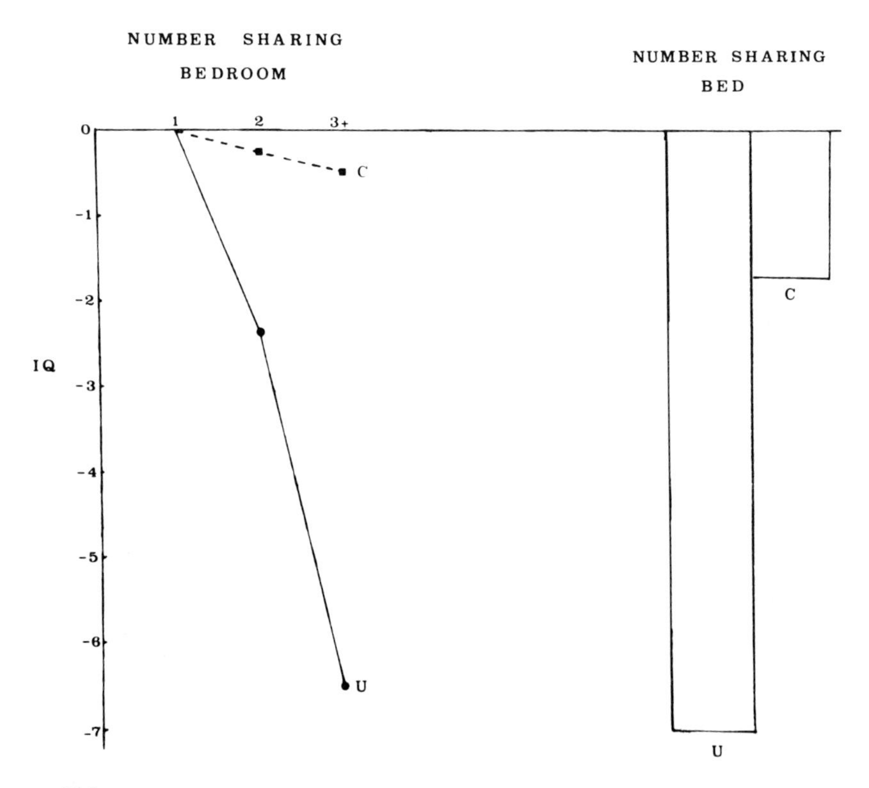

per cent of the children (n = 13725) shared a bed and 56.3 per cent shared a bedroom.

The results are presented in Figure 8. It can be readily seen that, before correction, both variables show a strong relationship to IQ score. After correction only bed-sharing showed a highly significant effect.

There remain two other factors which have been shown to contribute to disadvantage; housing type and income/poverty. The NCDS provides information on tenure, i.e. owner occupier (45.8 per cent) versus private rented and council (54.2 per cent) and type of accommodation, whole house or bungalow (89.8 per cent) versus flat, rooms or caravan (10.2 per cent) and several measures of financial situation. These include (a) whether the child is receiving free school meals (10.4 per cent), (b) if the family suffers from financial hardship (11.4 per cent), (c) father's

FIGURE 9
Children's IQ in relation to employment and financial status of parents.

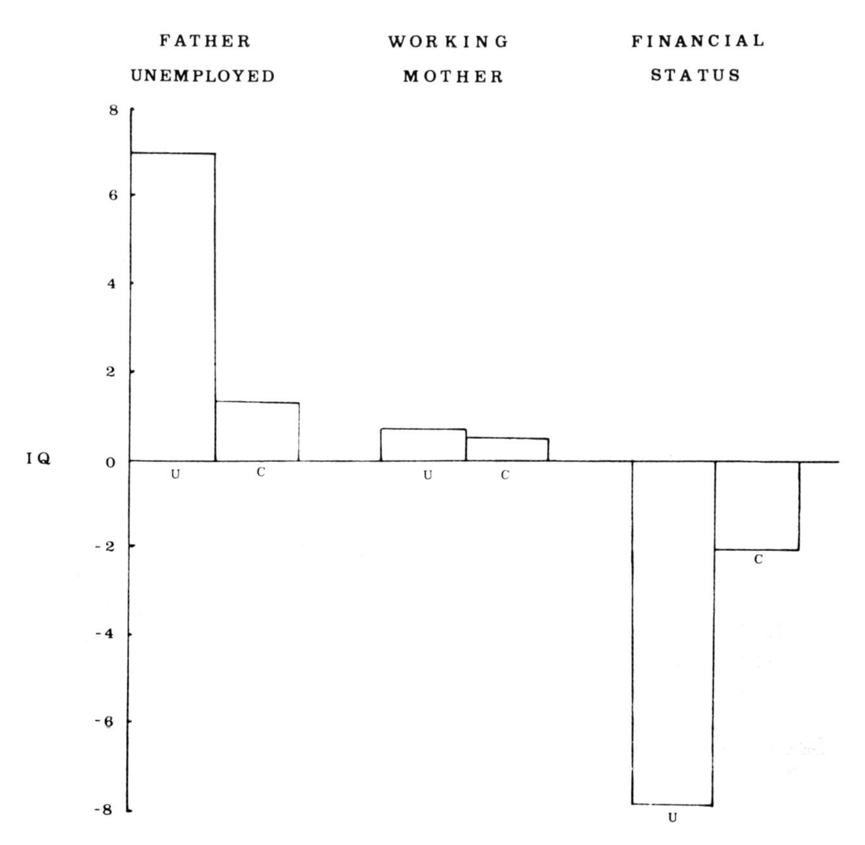

FIGURE 10
Effects of other social variables on children's IQ.

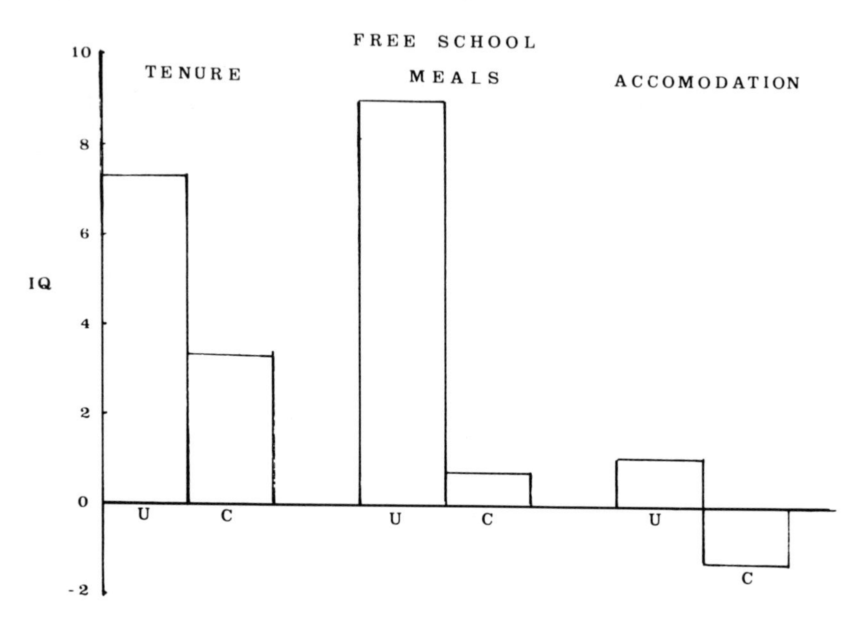

occupational status if employed (92.3 per cent) or unemployed (7.7 per cent) and (d) information on whether the mother is gainfully employed outside the home (61.4 per cent).

The results of these analyses are presented in Figures 9 and 10. The type of accommodation has only a slight effect on IQ score variation, whereas children of owner occupiers score nearly four IQ points higher on average than those living in privately rented or council houses even after correction. The four financial indices all show small effects, the most significant being financial status in those reporting hardship.

In summary the results clearly indicate that factors associated with disadvantage show a statistically independent relationship to IQ score. Consequently, a child who has free school meals, lives in a privately rented or council house, in overcrowded conditions (be it house, bedroom and bed) which lacks the basic amenities, whose father is unemployed and where there is financial hardship is, on average likely to have an IQ deficit well in excess of 16 IQ points.

Sex differences

It has been frequently suggested that there are sex differences in specific IQ components: girls are thought to be better on tasks involving verbal skills and boys on tasks involving visuo-spatial concepts (Maccoby and Jacklin, 1975). Figure 11 illustrates the IQ scores for total IQ as well as verbal and non-verbal scores. Boys' scores have been set to zero. Clearly girls score significantly higher on total and verbal IQ while the non-verbal mean is also in favour of girls. This might indicate that in this sample girls are generally better than boys at all tasks or might reflect an absence of the more visuo-spacial taks at which boys are thought to excel.

FIGURE 11
Sex differences in three measures of children's IQ. Data given are for girls, in relation to boys' score which is set at zero.

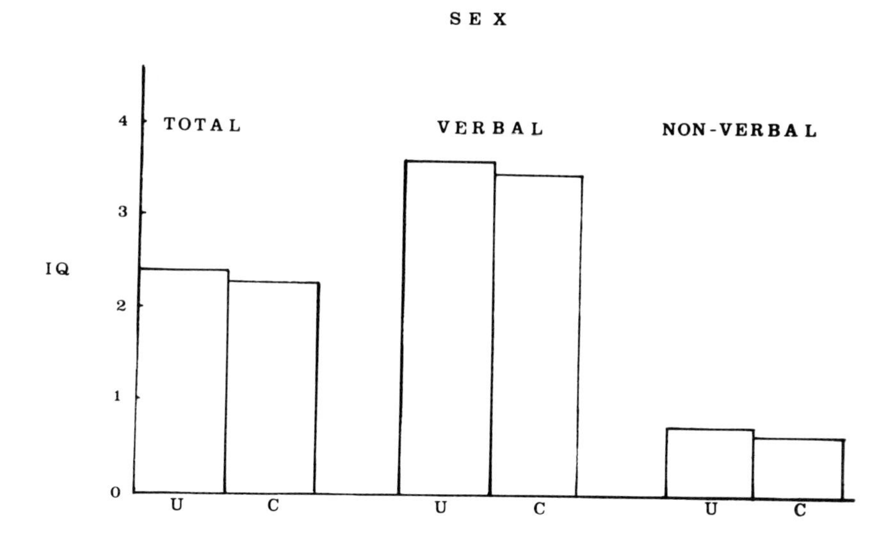

Lateralization

Sex differences in cognitive style have been related to different patterns of lateralization of function (Hutt, 1972). Reading defects have also been related to unusual patterns of eye-hand dominance (Corballis and Beale, 1976) and left handers in general have been suggested to be of lower overall ability (Hardyck *et al.,* 1976; Mascie-Taylor, 1980a). Differences in personality have also been found between left and right handers (Mascie-Taylor, 1981). Figure 12 presents the relationship between handedness and eye dominance and IQ score where left hand and eye IQ scores have been set to zero. Right handers score significantly higher than left handers, even after correction, while the relationship with eye dominance shows no significant laterality effect after correction.

FIGURE 12
Children's IQ in relation to parental status (i.e. not natural parents), and hand/eye laterality.

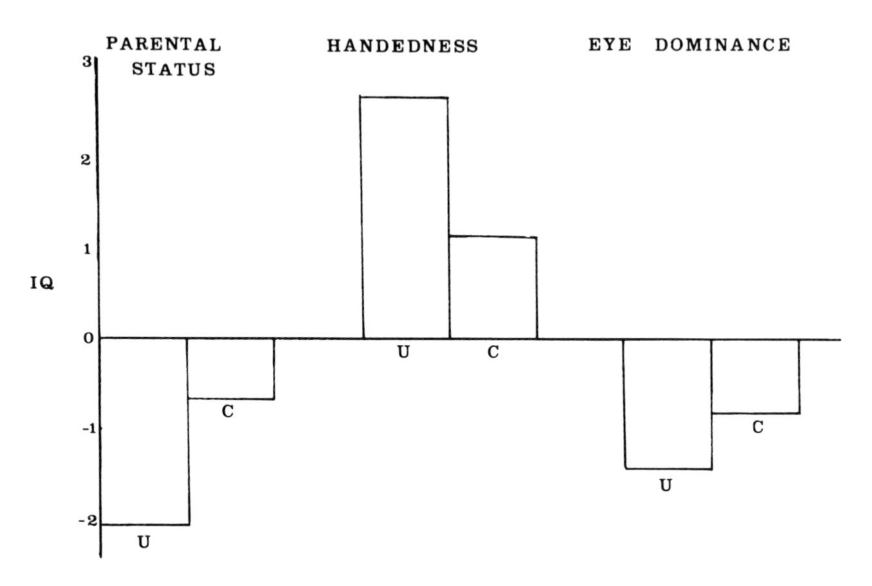

Parental status and age

Traditionally broken homes and prolonged parent-child separation have been seen as important factors predisposing to delinquency. Bowlby (1946) claimed that prolonged separation of a child from his mother stood foremost among the causes of delinquent character formation, although recent work has shown that it is not the separation or break-up as such which is most important.

It seemed worthwhile, given that information was available on parental status, to examine its relationship to IQ score. The analyses presented here merely differentiate between children who have both natural parents and the rest. (Other analyses (Mascie-Taylor, 1983, unpublished) have considered the type of parental status.) The results, presented in Figure 12 (setting the score for both natural parents to zero) suggest that there is a slight negative effect on children's IQ performance if both the parents are not the natural ones.

Parental age has also been reported to relate to cognitive ability. In a Dutch study, Zybert *et al.,* 1978, found a positive association between IQ and mother's age as did an American study (Broman *et al.,* 1975). The result obtained from this study (Figure 13) show a highly significant effect after correcting for all other variables (and of course, after

FIGURE 13
Relationships between parental age, and age difference (mother-father), and children's IQ score after correction for other variables.

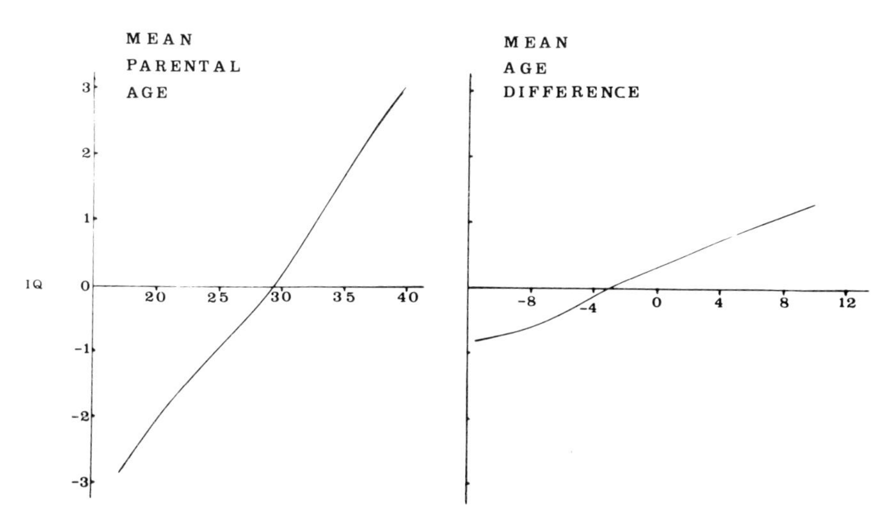

FIGURE 14
Relationship between children's height and IQ score, after correction for other variables including social class effects.

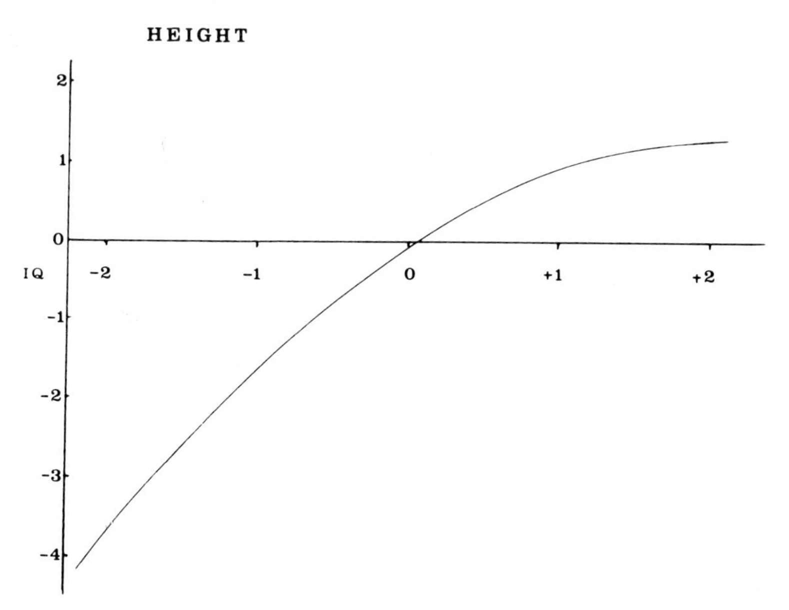

removal of known congenital and other defects). It is also interesting to see that mean age difference of parents also associates with IQ score. Families in which the mother is the older parent show a small but significant increase in relation to IQ score.

Height

Numerous studies have shown a consistent association between child's height and intelligence. Taller children are, on average, of greater intellectual ability (Tanner, 1969), although it has been suggested that this relationship is a reflection of social class differences (Rutter and Madge, 1976). The results of this survey, (Figure 14), indicate that after removal of social class effects (and 97 others) there still remains a highly significant relationship between height and IQ.

Moves of school and home

The evidence concerning the educational consequences of frequent moves of house and school is somewhat contradictory (Kantor, 1965). Douglas, 1964 found that school progress was not affected by frequent moves during the primary school period but children did less well at school if frequent moves occurred in the first five years. Catch up to some extent occurred by 11 years of age. The London Literacy Survey, (Inner London Education Authority, 1973) showed that children who had

FIGURE 15
Relationships between changes of school, and changes of residence, and children's IQ.

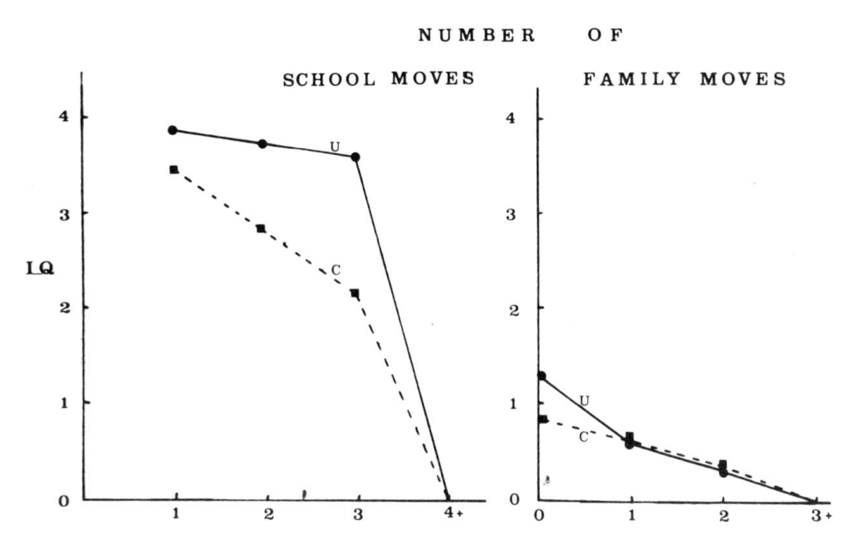

been to at least three schools by the age of eight or nine had lower reading scores than those who had attended only one or two schools. However, children of naval families who move home and school frequently show no educational deficit (Matthews, 1974).

The NCDS data indicates that family moves have little effect on child IQ whereas school moves do. Even after correction, children who attend four or more schools are on average 3.5 IQ points below those who only move once (Figure 15).

Regional variations

Studies in America have shown that reading difficulties are considerably more prevalent in areas of low social status and especially in deteriorating inner city areas (Miller *et al.,* 1957; Eisenberg, 1966) although this finding may reflect the low occupational status of the parents living in such areas.

In Britain, two surveys have shown that Scottish children have superior reading attainments than English children in spite of the greater proportion of lower middle class families in Scotland, but they had lower non-verbal intelligence test scores (Douglas, 1964; Davie *et al.,* 1972). Rutter and Madge suggest that it is uncertain whether this finding is due to the better school teaching of reading skills in Scotland, to greater involvement of Scottish parents in helping their children to read, or to other unknown factors.

Lynn, in a series of papers (Lynn, 1977, 1979a, 1979b) examined the regional variation of IQ in the British Isles. He reviewed much of the literature and set out to try and explain the low mean IQ in Scotland. He argued that the reduced IQ score in Scotland in contemporary times is largely the result of selective migration in the people who leave Scotland, the outmigrants (emigrants) having higher IQs than those who remain (the sedentes).

The results from the NCDS can be considered in two parts. Firstly an examination of regional variation in IQ scores at age 11 and secondly consideration of the evidence for selection migration from Scotland.

The regional variations in IQ score in the eleven standards regions are presented in Figure 16. Scotland together with the Northern and East and West Ridings have the lowest mean IQs. All IQs are measured as deviations from the grand mean which has been set to zero. These results are for regional variation in IQ score *per se.* After correction the scores shown in Figure 17 are obtained. Scotland now has the (relatively) highest mean! It would appear that the social and economic disadvantages do not depress the IQs of Scottish children as much as English children.

Turning to the question of migration the NCDS can be used to provide details on regional/geographical (and social) migration. Information is

FIGURE 16
Regional variation in Great Britain in children's IQ, expressed in deviations from the grand mean set at zero.

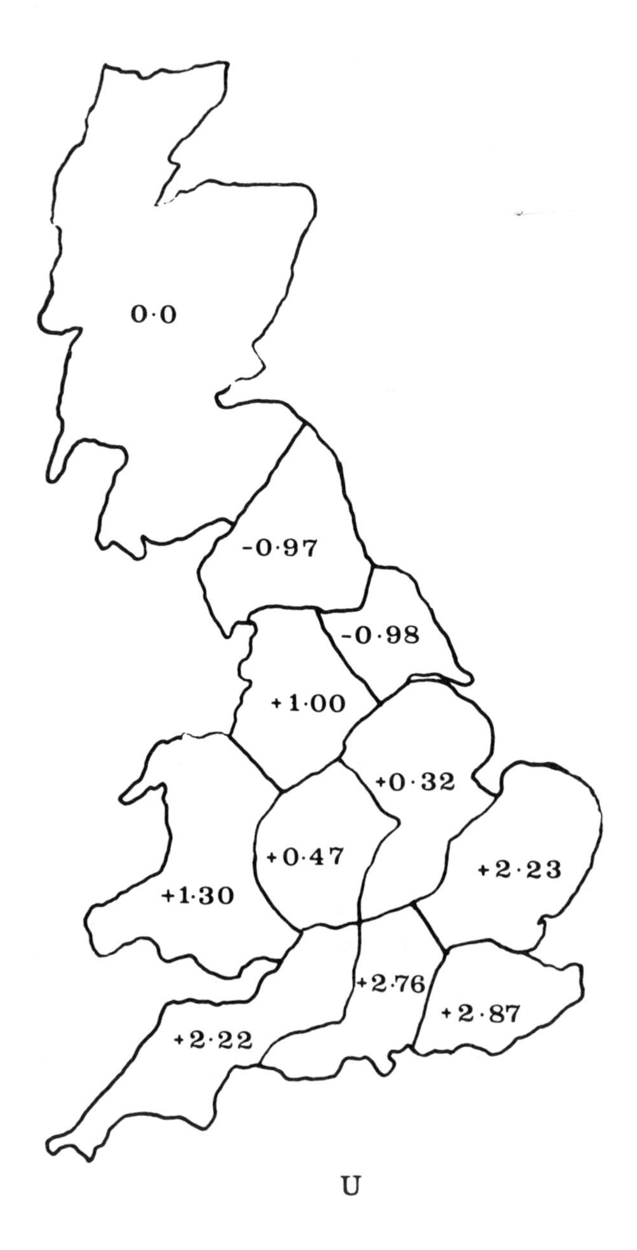

U

FIGURE 17
Regional variation in children's IQ after correction for social and economic factors.

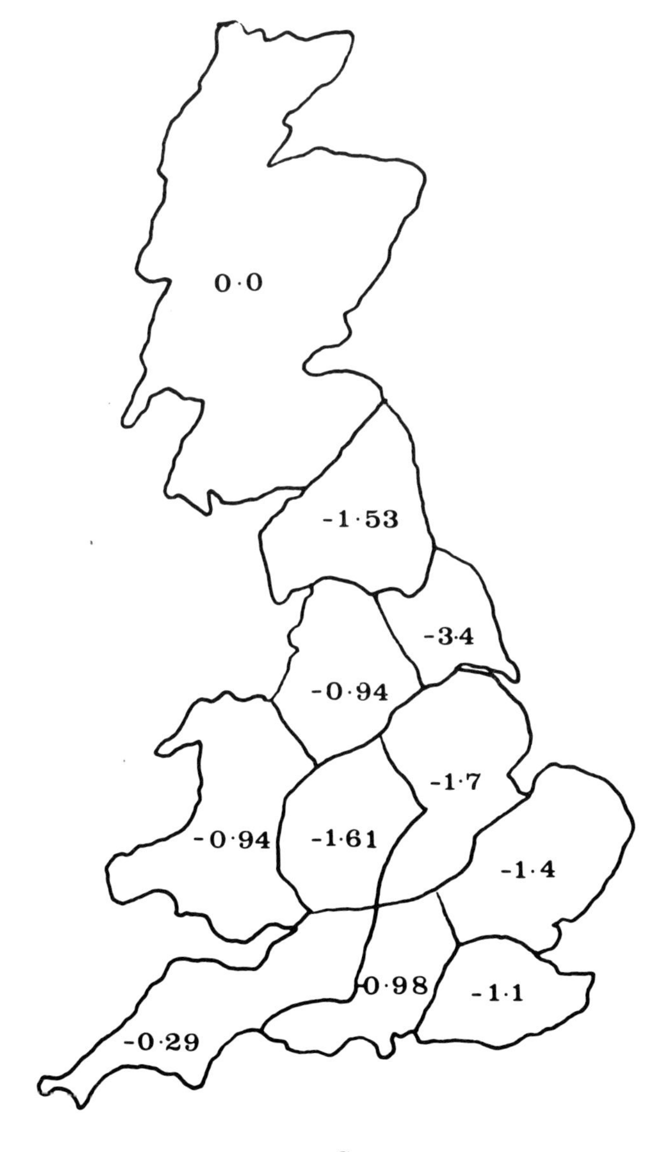

FIGURE 18
The IQ of children migrating from the regions of Great Britain, expressed as deviations from the IQ of sedentes.

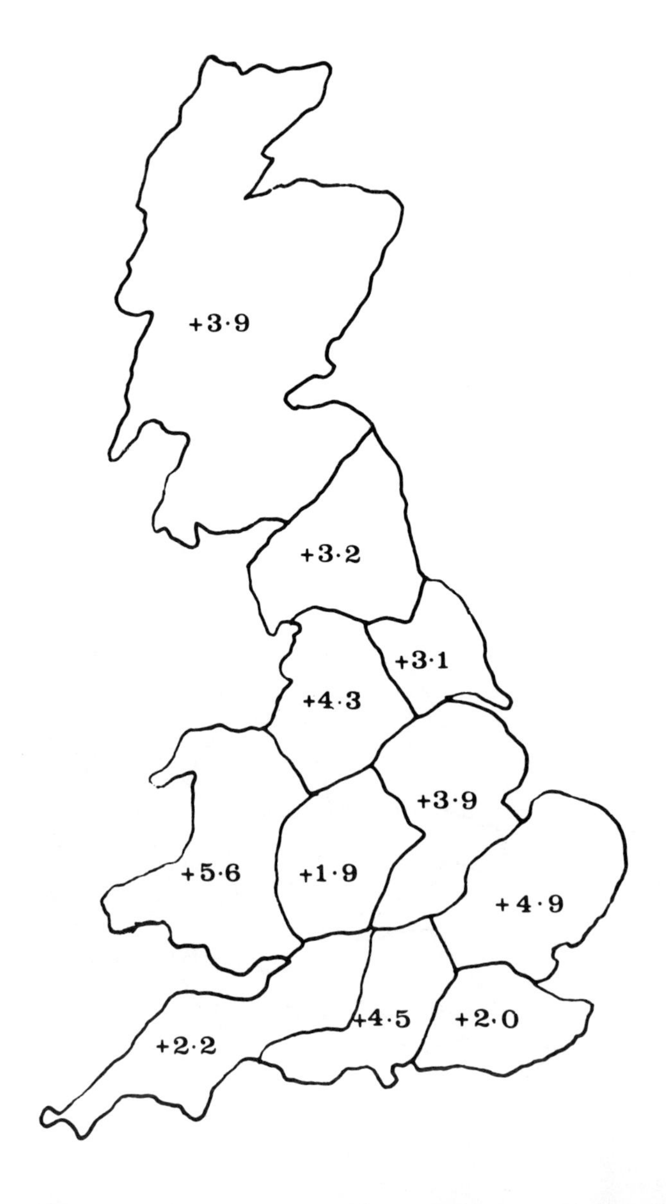

FIGURE 19
The IQ of children migrating into the regions of Great Britain, expressed as deviations from the IQ of sedentes.

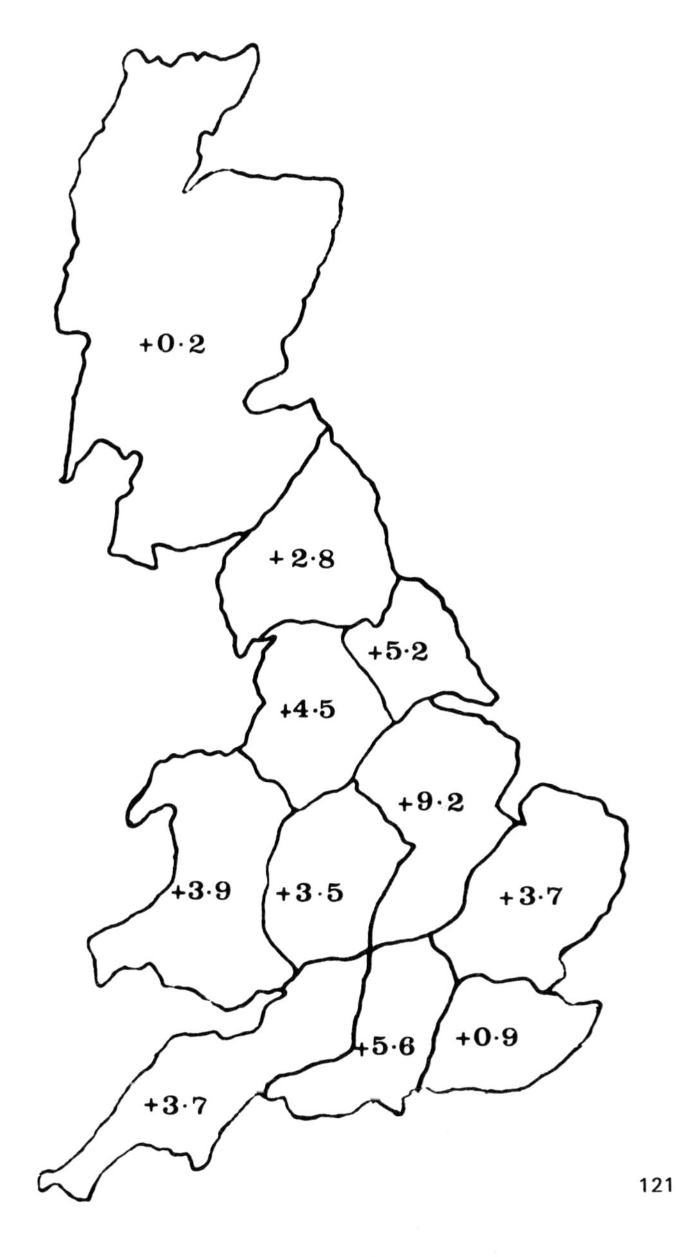

FIGURE 20
Regional variations in children's IQ as a result of in- and out-migration.

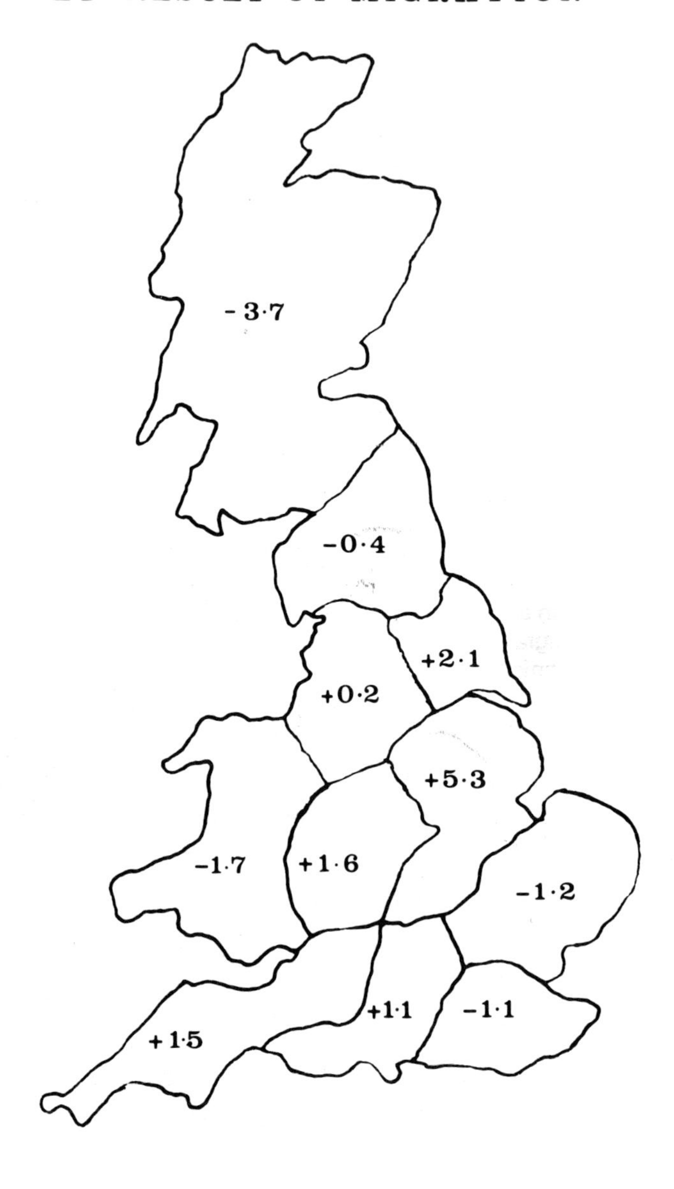

FIGURE 21
Deviations of children's IQ in relation to social and geographical mobility.

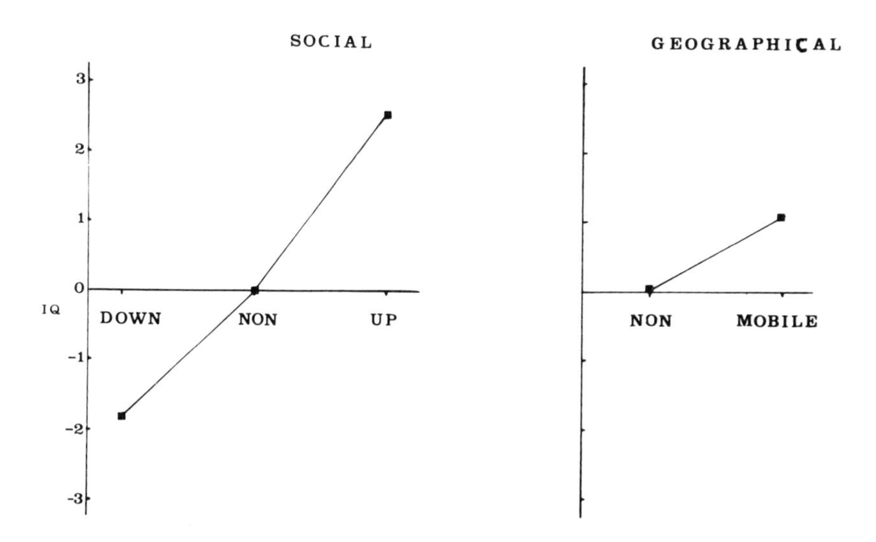

available on region at birth and region in which the child was living at age 11. Consequently it is possible to distinguish migrants and non-migrants between birth and age 11, i.e. between 1958 and 1969. Comparison of outmigrants with sedentes produces the results shown in Figure 18. All outmigrants had higher IQs than sedentes. Of course these outmigrants from one region must be immigrants to another (unless they left Britain). In-migration values are presented in Figure 19. All in-migrants have higher IQs than sedentes. Finally we can compute the net result of migration, outmigration minus inmigration. The results show clearly that Scotland is undergoing negative selective migration (as are Wales and the Northern, Eastern, London and South East regions) while others show marked positive selective migration particularly the North Midlands (Figure 20).

Social Mobility

The final variable considered is social mobility. Several studies have related movement between social classes to IQ scores, while later studies compared father-son IQ difference in relation to mobility. Sons with higher IQs than their fathers tended to be upwardly socially mobile, those with lower IQs non-mobile or downwardly mobile (Burt, 1961; Waller, 1971; Gibson, 1970; Anderson *et al.,* 1952; Gibson and Mascie-Taylor,

1973). Mascie-Taylor and Gibson (1978) found that there was a linear relationship between father and son IQ discrepancy and degree of social mobility. This result has been replicated recently (Gibson *et al.,* 1983).

For the NCDS data it seemed worthwhile relating socially mobile and non-mobile families and IQ score of the child. The results are presented in Figure 21. It is clear that after controlling for other main effects a significant relationship between IQ score and mobility still remains.

Discussion

This paper has examined the relationship between a large number of variables and IQ score variation of children at age 11. The findings can be summarized as follows:—

(1) Most variables showed a significant relationship to IQ score after controlling for 97 other main effects.

(2) The magnitude of this relationship in terms of IQ points was quite often small. This is to be expected (see (4).

(3) There was no evidence of any significant global interaction between variables, i.e. variables act additively, a result in keeping with previous findings (McManus and Mascie-Taylor, 1983; Mascie-Taylor, 1983b).

(4) Consequently if 30 variables each account for 0.5 IQ point, this is sufficient to explain up to one standard deviation in IQ score variation.

(5) The main effects described here produced a multiple correlation of 0.53 and thus accounted for 28.2 per cent of the variance of total IQ score. The R^2 is larger than those reported from other studies (Broman *et al.,* 1975; Vandenberg and Kuse, 1980; Firkowska, *et al.,* 1978). The main reasons for R^2 not being higher are that (a) no allowance is made for reliability or for reading and other attainments, (b) no information is available on parent IQs and hence parent-child IQs cannot be computed and (c) no allowance can be made for assortative mating (Mascie-Taylor and Gibson, 1979).

Acknowledgments

I am grateful to Mr. K. Fogelman and the National Children's Bureau for allowing me to re-analyse the data obtained by the National Child Development Study and to Mr. E. Roughley and the Social Sciences Research Council's Survey Archive for supplying the data.

I gratefully acknowledge financial support from the Marie Stopes Research Fund of the Eugenics Society.

References

Adams, B.N. (1972). Birth order: a critical review. *Sociometry,* 35, 411-422.

Adams, B., Ghodsian M. and Richardson, K. (1976). Evidence for a low upper limit of heritability of mental test performances in a national sample of twins. *Nature,* 263, 314.

Altus, W.D. (1966). Birth order and its sequelae. *Science,* 151, 44-49.

Anastasi, A. (1956). Intelligence and family size. *Psychological Bulletin,* 53, 187-209.

Anderson, C.A., Brown, J.C. and Bowman, M.J. (1952). Intelligence and occupational mobility. *Journal of Political Economy,* 40, 208-226.

Belmont, L. and Marolla, J.A. (1973). Birth order, family size and intelligence. *Science,* 182, 1096-1101.

Bowlby, J. (1946). *Forty-Four Juvenile Thieves: Their Characters and Home Life.* London: Baillière, Tindall & Cox.

Broman, S.H., Nichols, P.L. and Kennedy, W.A. (1975). *Preschool IQ: Prenatal and Early Developmental Correlates.* Hillsdale, New Jersey: Lawrence Erlbaum.

Burks, B.S. (1928). The relative influence of nature and nuture upon mental development: a comparative study of foster-parent — foster-child resemblance and true parent-child resemblance. *Yearbook of the National Society for the Study of Education,* 27, 219-316.

Burt, C. (1961). Intelligence and social mobility. *British Journal of Statistical Psychology,* 14, 1-34.

Butler, N.R. and Alberman, E.D. (Editors) (1969). *Perinatal Problems.* London: Livingstone.

Butler, N.R. and Bonham, D.G. (1963). *Perinatal Mortality.* London: Livingstone.

Clausen, J.A. (1966). Family structure, socialization and personality. In *Review of Child Development Research, Vol. 2,* edited by L.W. Hoffman and M.L. Hoffman. London: Russell Sage Foundation.

Corballis, M.W. and Beale, J.L. (1976). *The Psychology of Left and Right.* Hillsdale, New Jersey: Lawrence Erlbaum.

Dale, R.R. and Griffith, S. (1965). *Down Stream: Failure in the Grammar School.* London: Routledge & Kegan Paul.

Davie, R., Butler, N. and Goldstein, H. (1972). *From Birth to Seven: A report of the National Child Development Study.* London: Longman.

Deutch, M., Katz, I. and Jensen, A.R. (Editors) (1968). *Social Class, Race and Psychological Development.* New York: Holt, Rinehart & Winston.

Douglas, J.W.B. (1964). *The Home and the School.* London: MacGibbon & Kee.

Douglas, J.W.B., Ross, J.M. and Simpson, H.R. (1968). *All Our Future: A Longitudinal Study of Secondary Education.* London: Peter Davies.

Eisenberg, L. (1966). The classification of psychotic disorders in childhood. In *The Classification of Behaviour Disorders,* edited by L.D. Eron. Chicago: Aldine.

Firkowska, A., Ostrovska, A., Sokolowska, M., Stein, Z., Susser, M. and Wild, I. (1978). Cognitive development and social policy. *Science,* 200, 1357-1362.

Floud, J., Halsey, A.H. and Martin, F.M. (1956). *Social Class and Educational Opportunity.* London: Heinemann.

Fogelman, K. (1980). Smoking in pregnancy and subsequent development of the child. *Child Care, Health and Development,* 6, 233-242.

Fogelman, K. Goldstein, H., Essen, J. and Ghodsian, M. (1978). Patterns of attainment. *Educational Studies,* 4, 121-120.

Fogelman, K. (Editor) (1983). *Growing Up in Great Britain.* London: National Children's Bureau Series.

Gibson, J.B. (1970). Biological aspects of a high socio-economic group. I. IQ, education and social mobility. *Journal of Biosocial Science,* 2, 1-16.

Gibson, J.B., Harrison, G.A., Clarke, V.A. and Hiorns, R.W. (1973). ABO blood groups and IQ. *Nature,* 163, 878-879.

Gibson, J.B., Harrison, G.A., Hiorns, R.W. and Macbeth, H.M. (1983). Social Mobility and psychometric variation in a group of Oxfordshire villages. *Journal of Biosocial Science,* 15, 193-205.

Gibson, J.B. and Mascie-Taylor, C.G.N. (1973). Biological aspects of a high socio-economic group. II. IQ components and social mobility. *Journal of Biosocial Science,* 5, 17-30.

Hardyck, C. Petrinovich, L.F. and Goldman, R.D. (1976). Left-handedness and cognitive deficit. *Cortex,* 12, 266.

Hutt, C. (1972). *Males and Females* Harmondsworth, Middlesex: Penguin Books.

Inner London Education Authority (1973). *Literacy Survey: 1971 Follow-Up, Preliminary Report.* London: Inner London Education Authority.

Jones, H.E. (1933). Order of birth. In *A Handbook of Child Psychology,* edited by C.A. Murchison. Georgetown, Massachusetts: Clark University Press.

Kantor, M.B. (1965). Some consequences of residential and social mobility for the adjustment of children. In *Mobility and Mental Health,* edited by M.B. Kantor. Springfield, Illinois: Charles C. Thomas.

Kunz, P.R. and Peterson, C.T. (1973). Family size and academic achievement of persons enrolled in high school and the university. *Social Biology,* 20, 454-462.

Kunz, P.R. and Peterson, C.T. (1977). Family size, birth order and academic achievement. *Social Biology,* 24, 144-151.

Leahy, A.M. (1935). Nature-nurture and intelligence. *Genetic Psychology Monographs,* 17, 235-308.

Lieberman, J.E. (1970). Reserving the womb: case for the small family. *American Journal of Public Health,* 60, 87.

Lynn, R. (1977). Selective emigration and the decline of intelligence in Scotland. *Social Biology,* 24, 173-182.

Lynn, R. (1979a). The social ecology of intelligence in the British Isles. *British Journal of Social and Clinical Psychology,* 18, 1-12.

Lynn, R. (1979b). The geographical distribution of intelligence in the British Isles. *Eugenics Society Bulletin,* 11, 78-82.

Maccoby, E.E. and Jacklin, C.N. (1975). *The Psychology of Sex Differences.* London: Oxford University Press.

McManus, I.C. and Mascie-Taylor, C.G.N. (1983). Biosocial correlates of cognitive abilities. *Journal of Biosocial Science,* 15, 289-306.

Mascie-Taylor, C.G.N. (1977). Ph.D Thesis (unpublished).

Mascie-Taylor, C.G.N. (1980a). Hand preference and components of IQ. *Annals of Human Biology,* 7, 235-248.

Mascie-Taylor, C.G.N. (1980b). Family size, birth order and IQ components: a survey of a Cambridge suburb. *Journal of Biosocial Science,* 12, 309-312.

Mascie-Taylor, C.G.N. (1980c). Season of birth, IQ components and personality traits. *Journal of Genetic Psychology,* 137, 151-152.

Mascie-Taylor, C.G.N. (1981). Hand preference and personality traits. *Cortex,* 17, 319-322.

Mascie-Taylor, C.G.N. (1983a). *Parental Studies and IQ Variations* (unpublished).

Mascie-Taylor, C.G.N. (1983b). Social and geographical aspects of migration. In *Migration and Mobility,* edited by A.J. Boyce. London: Taylor & Francis.

Mascie-Taylor, C.G.N. and Gibson, J.B. (1978). Social mobility and IQ components. *Journal of Biosocial Science,* 10, 263-276.

Mascie-Taylor, C.G.N. and Gibson, J.B. (1979). A biological survey of a Cambridge suburb: assortative marriage for IQ and personality traits. *Annals of Human Biology,* 6, 1-16.

Mascie-Taylor, C.G.N., McManus, E.C., Maclarnon, A.M. and Laigan, P.M. (1983). The association between phenylthiocarbamide (PTC) tasting and psychometric variables. *Behavior Genetics,* 13, 191-196.

Mascie-Taylor, C.G.N., Gibson, J.B., Hiorns, R.W. and Harrison, G.A. (1984). The association between haptoglobin phenotypes and IQ test scores (submitted to *Behavior Genetics.*

Matthews, P.C. (1974). *Report of the (Seebohm) Naval Welfare Committee.* Appendix 6. London: Her Majesty's Stationery Office.

Miller, A.D., Margolin, J.B. and Yolles, S.J. (1957). Epidemiology of reading disabilities: some methodical considerations and early findings. *American Journal of Public Health,* 47, 1250-1256.

Nisbet, J.D. (1953). *Family Environment: A Direct Effect of Family Size on Intelligence.* London: The Eugenics Society.

Nisbet, J.D. and Entwistle, N.J. (1967). Intelligence and family size. *British Journal of Educational Psychology,* 37, 188-193.

Petzing, J. and Wedge, P.J. (1970). Homes fit for children? *New Society,* 16, 448-450.

Plowden, B. (1967). *Children and their Primary Schools.* London: Her Majesty's Stationery Office.

Rutter, M.L. and Madge, M. (1976). *Cycles of Disadvantage.* London: Heinemann Educational Books.

Rutter, M.L., Tizard, J. and Whitmore, K. (Editors) (1970). *Education, Health and Behaviour.* London: Longman.

Schooler, C. (1972). Birth order effects: not here, not now! *Psychological Bulletin,* 78, 161-175.

Skodak, M. and Skeels, H.M. (1949). A final follow-up study of one hundred adopted children. *Journal of Genetic Psychology,* 75, 85-125.

Tanner, J.M. (1969). Relation of body size, intelligence scores and social circumstances. In *Trends and Issues in Developmental Psychology,* edited by P.H. Mussen, J. Largen and M. Covington. New York: Holt, Rinehart & Winston.

Thoday, J.M. (1967). New insights into continuous variation. In *Proceedings of the Third International Congress of Human Genetics,* edited by J.F. Crow and J.V. Neel. Baltimore: Johns Hopkins.

Vandenberg, S.G. and Kuse, A.R. (1980). *In Search of the Missing Environmental Variance in Cognitive Ability.* Paper presented to the Third International Congress of Twin Studies, Jerusalem, 16-20 June, 1980.

Vernon, P.E. (1979). *Intelligence, Heredity and Environment.* San Francisco: W.H. Freeman.

Waller, J.H. (1971). Achievement and social mobility; relationships among IQ score, education and occupation in two generations. *Social Biology,* 18, 252-259.

Wray, J.D. (1971). *Population Pressure on Families, Family Size and Child Spacing in Rapid Population Growth: Consequences and Policy Implications.* Study Committee of the Office of the Foreign Secretary, National Academy of Sciences. Baltimore: Johns Hopkins.

Zajonc, R.B. (1976). Family configuration and intelligence. *Science* 192, 227.

Zybert, P., Stein, Z. and Belmont, L. (1978). Maternal age and children's ability. *Perceptual and Motor Skills,* 47, 815-836.

Cognitive Development in the Mentally Handicapped With Particular Reference to Down's Syndrome

BRIAN STRATFORD

School of Education, University of Nottingham, Nottingham

We know that it takes only a very small change in the cytogenetic coding to produce quite devastating pathological differences in the human person. In this respect there can be no doubt about it, children with Down's syndrome are different. It is just one extra chromosome on the twenty first pair which is responsible for producing the features, the stature and indeed the personality of these children. Most of us are familiar with the archetype and it is easy to recognise the condition, at least by sight. Yet it is less than 25 years since Lejeune and his colleagues (1959) discovered this specific genetic cause. And if this chromosome anomaly can have such an effect on that which we can see, it is only reasonable to suppose it will have some effect on the mental disposition of the child born with this condition. Of course we soon become aware that he is extremely retarded, but just as the physical features take a particular form might not the nature of the retardation have a particular form also?

Over the years there have been numerous attempts to find a 'cure', but in the nature of things, such attempts are bound to meet with as much success as the search for the philosopher's stone. All of them have come to naught, even those which, though not claiming to alter the structure of the cells, have hinted at miraculous changes as a result of attention to nutrition (e.g. Harrell *et al.,* 1981). What is not properly understood is that Down's syndrome is not a disease open to treatment but it is the child, the whole child in every aspect of his existence; just as a child who might be described in this society as 'normal' because he has, like the majority of his kind, a complement of 46 chromosomes. But we know of course that this admits of infinite variation in his growth and development. The degree of successful adaptation will depend to a large extent on his environmental conditions, circumstances and opportunities as well as on his initial genetic endowment. This is equally true of the Down's syndrome child. Though here the original genetic endowment is demonstrably impaired; or at least different. To seek to change this is as unrealistic as to seek to exchange our 'normal' child for another through the intervention of chemistry. Does this therefore mean that there is nothing we can do for the Down's syndrome child? Certainly not: but if we continue to act towards him as though he were not in any way different, it might satisfy our own psychological and social urges towards some kind of fabulous equality but it would be less than helpful to the Down's syndrome child. Rather, we should be seeking to learn more about the effects this arrangement of chromosomes has on his ability to grapple with the complexities of the learning process. And here there are more grounds for hope.

More and more evidence is being gathered which is helping us to understand better the strategies which these children adopt to come to terms with their world, and though the strategies are often inappropriate they are nearly always logical and sensible. In order to shift these inappropriate, rather than wrong, strategies to the more convenient, conventional and acceptable ones we need first of all to find some means of analysing and understanding them.

The experimental work reported in this paper attempts to throw some light on this problem. Firstly it must be said that all is not so neat and orderly as to suggest that Down's syndrome children do things this way and other children do them that way. No, nature is not so orderly, and particularly human nature. There is nothing which can be found in the learning and behaviour patterns of Down's syndrome children which cannot also be found in normal children. It is all a question of number and degree. We must equally beware of myth and folklore which can be as misleading and unproductive as expecting a Down's syndrome child to learn through methods found to be successful with normal children and applied with hope. Recent experimental evidence (Stratford and Ching, 1983) has gone some way towards exploding the myth that Down's syndrome children are musical and have 'a marked sense of rhythm'. The interesting fact emerges that there is no difference whatsoever between Down's syndrome and young normal children (matched on mental age). Actually, neither is very good and their sense of rhythm is certainly not 'marked'. The musical characteristic is probably accounted for by the finding that Down's syndrome children are significantly better than other mentally handicapped children. Though in view of the results of this research it may be more accurate to say that other mentally handicapped children are significantly worse.

Experimental Studies

Turning to studies related to fundamental differences in the learning behaviour of Down's syndrome children we can take just one or two examples from experimental work in the field of visual perception.

By the age of six months, Down's syndrome infants are already showing different preferences in their attention to visual stimuli than are normal children (Miranda and Fantz, 1973; 1974). Not only do Down's syndrome infants fix their attention on single aspects of a display where normal infants sample widely, they also show a distinct preference for simple stimuli and avoid complex patterns. This kind of behaviour continues into later childhood (Stratford, 1980; Stratford and Alban Metcalfe, 1981). It has also been shown (House and Zeaman, 1959; 1960) that errors which Down's syndrome children make in attempts to reproduce visually perceived forms are more likely to arise from these specific attention deficits than from perceptual inaccuracies. Attention is directed to irrelevancies or to parts of the display only. As a result, only a limited amount of information is processed. This frequently causes reproduction errors which can easily be misinterpreted as having resulted from some disorder in the perceptual system. A popular theory is that Down's syndrome children are particularly prone to reversals. This is not altogether surprising as many young normal children exhibit this tendency. Uncritical observation would tend to support this theory, but questions must be asked; is this due to perceptual distortion or does some other perceptual strategy play a part? How frequently do Down's syndrome children present this problem and is it a problem associated with other mentally handicapped children?

An experiment was conducted with a large number of children drawn from three groups, Down's syndrome, normal and other mentally handicapped children. (Table I).

TABLE I

Characteristics of experimental population: M.A. Range 2.5-7.0

Subjects	No.	Chronological age			Mental age	
		range	mean	sd	mean	sd
Down's syndrome	118	5.6-17.5	10.6	3.92	4.9	1.36
Non-Down's syndrome	108	5.9-17.1	11.2	5.10	4.6	1.42
Normal	123	3.6- 8.0	5.0	1.36	4.8	1.21

Three squares were cut from masonite and painted bright red. The squares were in increasing sizes, 12cm; 14cm; 16cm. They were presented in all six combinations and the subjects were each time invited to copy the arrangement using an identical set, first with the stimulus arrangement exposed and then from memory when the arrangement had been covered.

Full statistical details are in the published accounts of this experiment, both as a small scale study and one involving all the children described in Table I (Stratford, 1979a; Stratford and Alban Metcalfe, 1982). For the purposes of this paper it is sufficient to describe the overall outcome.

It has been stated earlier, and there is a good deal of evidence supporting the proposition, that mentally handicapped children attend to 'bits' of information and ignore the total configuration. Generally speaking the results of this experiment lent further support to this observation. However, there was one distinct exception and this exception was particularly evident in the Down's syndrome children. In four out of the six combinations, failures were due to the effect of trying to remember three

TABLE II

Numbers and percentages of monotonic 1.2.3. or 3.2.1. responses

(a) Subjects reversing orders 1.2.3. or 3.2.1.

	Matching		Memory	
	No.	%	No.	%
Down's syndrome	56	23.73	94	39.83
Non-Down's syndrome	28	12.96	31	14.35
Normal	6	2.44	12	4.88

(b) Subjects reversing both orders 1.2.3. and 3.2.1.

	Matching		Memory	
	No.	%	No.	%
Down's syndrome	10	4.23	23	9.74
Non-Down's syndrome	4	1.85	4	1.85
Normal	0	0.00	4	1.65

(c) Orders 1.2.3. or 3.2.1. imposed when stimulus model was neither of those. Number of times this occurred and percentages.

	Matching		Memory	
	No.	%	No.	%
Down's syndrome	32	6.78	73	15.46
Non-Down's syndrome	9	2.08	15	3.47
Normal	6	1.22	10	2.00

separate items of information, but the remaining two were in the stepped order of small to large or *vice-versa* (1 2 3 : 3 2 1) and were probably seen as 'wholes'. Errors in these orders were in the form of reversals.

The figures in Table II speak for themselves. In both tasks more Down's syndrome subjects than subjects from the other groups showed consistent reversals: proportionately at least twice as commonly in the matching task, at least five times as commonly in the memory task.

Without further consideration it could be assumed that here was proof that when Down's syndrome children formed *gestalten* they were either neurologically or psychologically predisposed to reverse images. But further consideration raised doubts about this explanation. For instance, it does not explain why it occurred spasmodically (Table II, (a)) and less frequently in both arrangements (Table II, (b)). Nor did it explain why a significantly high proportion of Down's syndrome subjects imposed one of these monotonic arrangements when neither had been presented, (Table II, (c)). Further investigation was called for. Wertheimer (1960), following the Gestalt School, observed that under experimental conditions visual patterns and dimly seen forms tend to be perceived as symmetrical, or meaningful, even when the displays presented were not so. The Gestalt School would maintain that there exists a natural tendency to organise, or re-organise, what is perceived into configuration which satisfy a basic need for 'goodness of fit', or 'good form'. In other words, perception is characterised by the law of totality. In the experiment described above it appeared that attention had been given to the total configuration of monotonic orders but these had frequently been matched or recalled in a reverse order. If now instead of regarding reversal of the 1 2 3 stepped pattern in terms of *reversal,* we regard this arrangement as one constituting 'good form', and if it were 'good form' which attracted Down's syndrome children, then the chance of presenting this either way is equal. It is monotonic either way and in fact a reversal could be thought of as producing a good and complete symmetrical type of 'answer'. If it were true that the Down's syndrome children were attracted to the good form of the monotonic order, and the imposition of such an order when this was not presented could suggest this, then there should exist a similar attraction to symmetry. A good symmetrical display cannot easily be reversed but this is always possible with an asymmetrical display.

Twenty five children from each group took part in an experiment. The apparatus consisted of ten 6cm sq. glossy red plastic pieces. Five of these were given to the subject and five were retained by the experimenter. Five pieces were laid out in a particular pattern and the subjects were asked to reproduce this; the stimulus remained in view during the attempt at reproduction. There were three different displays for each subject. One display was symmetrical and the other two were

FIGURE 1
The Three Displays

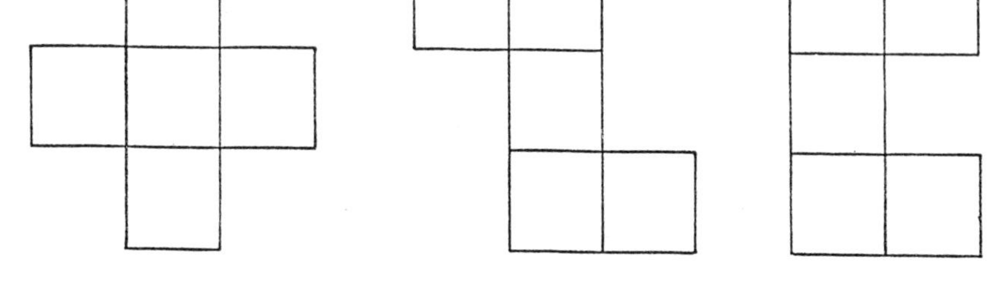

asymmetrical (see Figure 1). The order of presentation was alternated from subject to subject. The same procedure was then repeated though this time with the stimulus being concealed after the subject had seen it (Stratford, 1979b).

The most important element to examine in the results of this experiment is the kind of errors rather than the number of successes, though this can be deduced from Table III which gives a general picture of the results. It was attraction to symmetry which was under investigation and not the success or failure to reproduce the displays. In fact, in terms

TABLE III

Results. Number of symmetrical type errors

Subjects	Conditions	Matching Task		Memory Task		Total Sym. Type Errors	
		Errors	Sym. type	Errors	Sym. type	Matching	Memory
Down's	1	18	17	20	18		
Syndrome	2	24	17	23	20		
$n = 25$	3	9	6	6	4	40	42
Normal	1	11	8	13	8		
$n = 25$	2	17	9	13	7		
	3	5	2	5	2	19	17
Non-D.S.	1	16	11	16	10		
subnormal	2	24	13	21	15		
$n = 25$	3	9	5	6	5	29	30

of the experiment, the recording of successful reproductions could prove misleading. For example, only five Down's syndrome children correctly matched the symmetrical display (condition 1) but seventeen imposed an error which was symmetrical.

Certainly the symmetrical stimulus influenced a symmetrical response even if there was no correspondence. In place of the 'cross' display nine children arranged their display in the pattern of a five on a dice.

Errors were divided into those which were symmetrical and those which were asymmetrical whether or not they corresponded to one of the displays in the experiment. Analysis of variance showed no significant differences between the groups in their production of symmetrical or asymmetrical displays. The Down's syndrome and other mentally handicapped children had a numerically greater tendency to produce symmetrical models, particularly in the memory task where this group almost reached significance level. There was very little difference in aysmmetry by attraction in any group. There was no interaction between the groups and it is interesting to see that *all* groups are attracted to symmetry. The real difference was in the *extent* to which each group was attracted to symmetry and away from asymmetry and in this respect there can be no doubt that Down's syndrome children have a much greater tendency than other children. The profiles shown in Figure 2 help to make this clear. Reversals of asymmetrical displays were so few that they were hardly worth recording.

The most obvious conclusion to be drawn on the evidence of this experiment is that Down's syndrome children are significantly attracted to symmetrical arrangements, or 'good form'. The suggested reversal tendency of Down's syndrome children was not upheld. In fact the two asymmetrical conditions invited reversal had this been a specific characteristic. There were only six reversals (four by Down's syndrome and two by other mentally handicapped children) in condition 3, and three reversals in condition 2 (one Down's syndrome and two normals). Condition 3 presented few problems for any group, though this was balanced by the difficulties encountered in condition 2. Many more errors were made than might have been expected, so it would be safe to assume that these reversals occurred by chance. Why so many errors? Five pieces of equal size and colour, arranged as they were so as to make 'wholes' make it more difficult to attend to the separate pieces than it had been in the experiment concerned with three separate sizes. It may well be that the display is initially seen as a 'whole', but to assemble the same from separate parts proves too complex a task. In other words, there is a breakdown between the correctly perceived totality of the configuration and the details of its form. When this breakdown of integration occurs, the resulting execution is frequently another configuration which adheres to the principle of 'good form'.

FIGURE 2
Groups and categories: attraction to symmetry.
Category X — Symmetry; Category Y — Asymmetry.
A — Down's Syndrome; B — Non-Down's Syndrome; C — Normal.

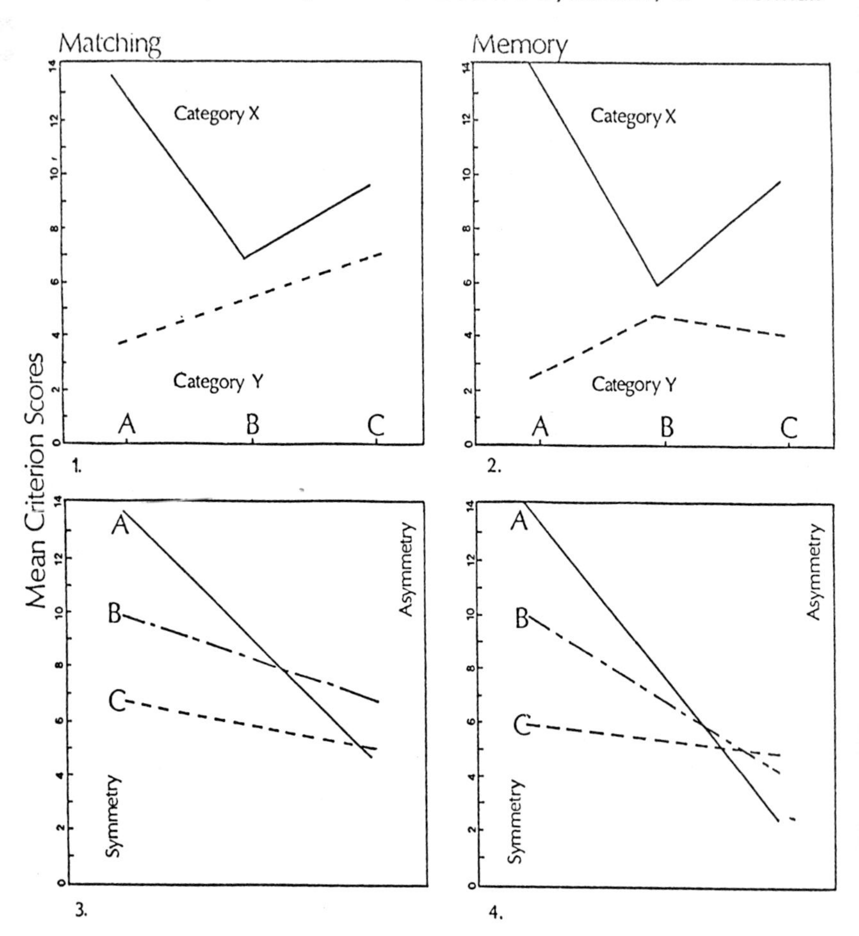

A further, and in some respects quite disturbing example of difference comes from some very recent work on the effect of time taken to complete a task (Stratford and Alban Metcalfe, 1983). Shortly stated, this research takes as its basis the fact that as normal children grow in years and intelligence the time taken to complete tasks steadily decreases. It was expected that Down's syndrome children would perform in a similar way but that there would be wider differences. The surprising finding was that Down's syndrome children produced no rational pattern at all when the dimension of time was added. It would, of course, be rash to attempt explanation without further research but the researchers have concluded that a striking feature among Down's syndrome subjects is the heterogeneity of variance in time taken to complete a task, and suggest that: (a) timed tasks do not afford very reliable measures of perceptual or cognitive functioning, and (b) timed and untimed tasks are measuring different aspects of perceptual and cognitive functioning; perhaps both these things. If it should turn out that timing does not afford a meaningful dimension for measuring performance in Down's syndrome children, there will have to be some re-thinking by those who base their assessments on the results of standardized tests.

Conclusions

Research findings, such as the examples described in this paper, and there are many others, have quite clear implications for teachers and others concerned with the development of mentally handicapped children. Organisation and classifying complex visual information is too difficult for these children to manage without careful attention to teaching strategies. When the system of organisation breaks down, it does not do so completely, but substitutes for correct classification and identification the simpler system of symmetrical order, and this is more easily learnt. Whether correctly or incorrectly depends on the demands of the task and its 'correct' solution. If the solution happened to be symmetrical, the result will be more likely to be correct because of the symmetrical arrangement than because a discrimination principle has been established. Mittler (1979) has said:

> "Recent developments have opened up a wide range of opportunities for teaching. The application of systematic methods of developmental planning, based on thorough assessment of the needs of each child as an individual, has shown that the development of even the most profoundly handicapped can be actively fostered. It is equally clear that it is not enough merely to expose children to the condition of learning . . ."

Many of our most severely handicapped Down's syndrome children may never achieve much beyond the sensori-motor stage of development, but small achievements in the primitive levels of cognition can have great effects on self confidence and enhance the well being of the individual. The experimental work reported in this paper is an illustration of the need for researchers and teachers to cooperate; for research and practice should go hand in hand. However carefully designed and carried out is the experimental work, it can never be regarded as truly completed until it has been transferred from the laboratory to the classroom. There need be no dichotomy between research and care. It is through the proper application of principles and methods resulting from research findings that the care provided by the teacher can be richer, more rewarding, and a great deal more effective.

References

Harrell, R.F., Capp, R.H., Davis, D.R., Peerless, J. and Ravitz, L.R. (1981). Can nutritional supplements help mentally retarded children? An exploratory study. *Proceedings of the National Academy of Science, USA,* 78(1), 574-578. Medical Sciences.

House, B.J. and Zeaman, D. (1959). Positive discrimination and reversals in low grade retardation. *Journal of Comparative and Physiological Psychology,* 52, 564.

House, B.J. and Zeaman, D. (1960). Visual discrimination learning and intelligence in defectives of low mental age. *American Journal of Mental Deficiency,* 65, 51.

LeJeune, J., Gautier, M. and Turpin, R. (1959). Etudes des chromosomes somatiques de neuf enfants mongoliens. *Academie des Sciences, Compt Rendus.* 248, 1721.

Miranda, S.B. and Fantz, R.L. (1973). Visual preferences in Down's Syndrome and normal infants. *Child Development,* 44, 555.

Miranda, S.B. and Fantz, R.L. (1974). Recognition and memory in Down's Syndrome and normal infants. *Child Development,* 45, 651.

Mittler, P. (1979). *Teaching Children with Severe Learning Difficulties.* Costello Educational, Tunbridge Wells.

Stratford, B. (1979a). Discrimination of size, form and order in Down's Syndrome and other mentally handicapped children. *Journal of Mental Deficiency Research,* 23, 45.

Stratford, B. (1979b). Attraction to 'good form' in Down's Syndrome. *Journal of Mental Deficiency Research,* 23, 243.

Stratford, B. (1980). Preferences in attention to visual cues in Down's Syndrome and normal children. *Journal of Mental Deficiency Research,* 24, 57.

Stratford, B. and Alban Metcalfe, J. (1981). Position cues in discrimination behaviour of normal, Down's Syndrome and othe mentally handicapped children. *Journal of Mental Deficiency Research,* 25, 89.

Stratford, B. and Alban Metcalfe, J. (1982). Recognition, reproduction and recall in children with Down's Syndrome. *Australia & New Zealand Journal of Developmental Disabilities,* 8, 125.

Stratford, B. and Ching, E. (1983). Rhythm and time in the perception of Down's Syndrome Children. *Journal of Mental Deficiency Research,* 27, 23-38.

Stratford, B. and Alban Metcalfe, J. (1983). Development of size judgement ability among Down's Syndrome and normal children. Paper presented at the *International Society for the Study of Behavioural Development.* Seventh Biennial Congress, Munich, Germany.

Wertheimer, M. (1960). *Productive Thinking.* London: Tavistock Publications.

Gifted Children

JOAN FREEMAN
Department of Education, University of Manchester; Manchester

The question of intellectual giftedness in children brings all the familiar complaints about educational selection to a head, varying from the objectivity of any tests, to the ethics of doing it at all. It is worth noting, though, that these strongly voiced objections do not apply to other areas of outstanding ability in children, such as athletics or music, especially where competition is involved. Despite growing interest from the Department of Education and Science, there is still no educational policy for the intellectually gifted in Britain to balance the concern for those at the lower end of the ability range.

Most teachers appear to be wary of elitism, whether of intellect (or wealth), being uncertain as to who the gifted are and less than clear as to what they might require (Oglivie, 1973; Department of Education and Science, 1977; Freeman, 1979). Many describe how distinguishing highly able children for educational purposes can have unwelcome side effects on the others, such as spreading inferiority complexes. This mental set against even the recognition of giftedness is pervasive.

Like any other phenotype, potential intellectual giftedness has to function in an environment from conception throughout development; the genotype always being inferred. Intellect is exceptional however, in being entirely dependent on culture for its expression. What the IQ tests are trying to measure is the amount of uptake of that culture — the profit — which the child has absorbed and can reproduce. I will go on to provide some evidence which suggests that for very highly able children, that potential *uptake* can be relatively more than for those of normal ability.

The primary problem in the identification of children as intellectually gifted is one of measurement. In research populations children are most frequently identified by an IQ cut-off point at widely varying levels. Although the concept of intelligence in any of its different styles of presentation and assessment cannot be all-embracing in describing the richness of intellectual life, it does appear to be the crucial thread which runs through most high abilities of all kinds.

Unfortunately, though, the psychologists who built the intelligence tests over the last half century were not immune from the effects of their times, and some of their outdated and specifically national assumptions are still practised. It is because of this cultural fallibility, and in spite of the high reliability and good predictive capabilities of the tests, that they cannot be taken as a true measure of intellectual potential for all children. An attempt is being made in some American states to overcome this problem and select children as gifted by minimising the influence of socio-cultural factors on their IQ scores. This is done by devising customised intelligence tests for recognised minority groups (Mercer and Lewis, 1978). Children are now selected for special gifted education programmes on those tests, who would score as below average on nationally standardised tests. However, the initial decision, as to which test to use for which child, presents obvious problems.

Intelligence is constantly affected by environmental conditions (Cicourel *et al.,* 1974). In circumstances of deprivation it appears to decline over time (Jensen, 1974; Clarke, 1980), though it can sometimes be resuscitated (Clarke and Clarke, 1976). But could even the most supportive conditions ever lead to giftedness? Can you make a silk purse out of a sow's ear, as the American, Glen Doman, has claimed? It has yet to be shown.

Socio-economic class influences on intellectual functioning can be seen however in the cumulative gap between potential and achievement (Douglas, 1968; Davie *et al.,* 1972). They were illustrated for me by this true story. There were once three boys, each with a Stanford-Binet IQ score of 170, whom I met in their first year class at Manchester Grammar School. The first one was the son of a doctor and a dentist and he eventually went up to Oxford, the second was of middle range parents and he went to a redbrick university, but the third was the son of a lathe turner and he left school at 16 for a day release course.

Studies of the concordance of monozygotic twins, separated at birth, are considered to reflect their common genetic make-up, though of course they share all the problems of unifying biological and behavioural science, where many features may be congenital or due to an inextricable combination of influences. The usual basis for comparison of the twins' intellectual capacity is the IQ score, and criticisms of its use in these studies are two-pronged: not only are the tests tapping more environmental effects than are recognised, but the research methodology in this area is out of date and badly flawed by present standards (Kamin, 1974; Adams *et al.,* 1976).

Many studies have considered environmental effects to be what was left over when the genetic relationship had been calculated, though sometimes such matters were investigated in a relatively superficial way by questionnaire. However sophisticated they are, present day recalculations of the old material must still be limited by the original research design (Kline, 1980), though contemporary investigation is making considerable attempts to cover the broader context of intellectual functioning (Davie, 1982). I believe that studies of genetic and environmental influences on intellectual behaviour, which do not investigate the children's home and school circumstances, that is, their all-round educational environment, cannot be providing a complete picutre and are therefore of suspect validity.

The effects of environment and heredity on intellectual giftedness can be usefully considered in terms of R.B. Cattell's concepts of 'Fluid' and 'Crystallised' intelligence (Freeman, 1983a). He has described 'Fluid' intelligence as being constitutional and measurable by 'culture free' tests, which tap the ability to judge relationships. The 'crystallised' form is the more information-loaded and can be measured with conventional intelligence tests (Cattell and Cattell, 1960). The relative differences between a child's results on tests of 'Fluid' and 'Crystallised' intelligence should, in theory, provide an indication of how far his or her intellectual potential is being fulfilled.

At all ages, the standard deviation of 'Fluid' intelligence has been found to be about twice that for the 'Crystallised' form, suggesting that scholastic type knowledge is relatively constricted, which Cattell has suggested (Cattell and Butcher, 1968, p.331) was 'making the bright mark time, to put pressure on the dull', and which he has also described as the 'law of conversion to the biosocial mean' (Cattell, 1971).

The Gulbenkian Project on Gifted Children

This was a project which studied highly able children in their home and school environments (Freeman, 1979) and its most recent findings are presented here. Its contribution to the furtherance of eugenic understanding was in its environmental approach to the children concerned, rather than working from a calculated base of modified genes. The detailed collection of environmental data provided a numerical estimate of the children's life circumstances with which to gauge how it had affected their intellectual development.

The initial sample of children was taken from the collection of records of the first eight years of The National Association for Gifted Children (NAGC). The jumbled, dusty box-files containing 4,500 sets of correspondences took a whole year to sort. Carnarvon must have had much the same experience when he entered the inner sanctum of Tutenkamen's tomb. Although my find was admittedly less exciting than his, it did provide me with a sample of children, whose parents believed they were gifted, from across the country.

I then selected a Target sample of 70 of these NAGC children using the criteria that all the children's parents had joined the association within the previous four years, the children were between 5 and 15 years old and they lived in the geographical area of North West England. Each of these Target group children was then matched for age and sex with two of their classmates as Controls, but whereas one of the Control children was matched for intellectual ability, the other was taken at random to provide an indication of the average class ability level. This matching was done with large scale screening, using Raven's Progressive Matrices at the appropriate level (Raven, 1965) — a recognised measure of Fluid intelligence. It made up a research population of 210 children and their parents, 61 schools and their class and head teachers: in all about 750 people.

From rural Cumbria to the south of Derbyshire and into the cities of Liverpool and Manchester, every home and school was visited at least once. There were 99 rated points in the final questionnaire for parents, which ranged over the relatively objective data on the child's milestones and parent's and grandparent's own education, number of books in the home, etc. to parent-child relationships, how they felt their own experiences had affected their attitudes to their children's education, family lifestyles and a brief, subjective (though rated) report by the researcher on the domestic scene.

A considerable attempt was made to make the children feel part of the project and they were mostly talked with and tested in their homes, where they felt comfortable. Much research with children, takes place in schools or offices, and children are rarely asked their opinions. But in fact, it proved to be most illuminating to hear what they had to say. Their questionnaire, which provided a further 49 rated points, was designed to examine the way they felt about their lives and other people; their attitudes, interests and deep thoughts, such as about God and the future. They were also tested on the Stanford-Binet Intelligence Scale (Terman and Merrill, 1961), Cattell's (IPAT) Personality Questionnaires (Porter and Cattell, 1959) and special ability tests.

In the schools, the headteachers were interviewed about such matters as their attitudes towards intellectual giftedness and how they organised their educational priorities, to provide a general picture of the children's formal educational situation. Each class teacher filled in the Bristol Social Adjustment Guides (Stott, 1967) for the three sample children in her class, which described their everyday behaviour.

Eventually 187 distinct variables became available to be analysed, factorially, by analysis of variance with orthogonal comparisons, and other non-parametric methods (Freeman, 1980).

Adjustment

When the Target children, who had been parent-identified as gifted, were compared with their two Control classmates of both equal and random ability, they were found to have more emotional problems. Significantly, the reasons for which these children had been identified as gifted were not so much to do with their ability as with their unwelcome social behaviour (Freeman, 1983b).

A close relationship between emotional disturbance and giftedness was often described to me (patiently as to a child) by parents and teachers during the research, and the idea had obviously been effective in the selection of these children as gifted. Terman's (1925) conclusions about the superior emotional adjustment of the gifted did not seem to apply here, and as his original Californian sample has often been criticised as being biased to the children of academics, maybe it was true that gifted children have more adjustment problems than those of average ability. But my hunch was that this was not so.

I took the whole sample of children out of their original Target and Control groups, and re-examined them on the basis of their IQ scores alone. Comparisons were made between those children placed in a high IQ group with a cut-off of IQ 140+, averaging an IQ of 155, and those in the lower range moderate IQ group with an average IQ of 120.

TABLE I

Children in the High and Moderate IQ groups

Group	*n*	Mean IQ	*sd*
High	82	155.012	9.903
Moderate	128	119.797	11.589

Many printouts later, quite another picture emerged. The children with the highest IQ scores were not the ones with the emotional difficulties — that accolade went to those with the most disturbed home backgrounds — across the sample ability range of IQ 100 to 170. Now the results were in line with those of Terman and of other researchers. Nor were there any worthwhile personality differences between the IQ groups, unlike those Cattell (1980) had found using the same measures, other than a described sensitivity among the most gifted. In essence, the difference between the gifted and the others was of ability, and a very high intelligence could not be said to be an emotional handicap.

When the High and Moderate IQ groups were examined with the environmental variable a strong positive association was apparent between social-class and IQ score. In addition, as the grandparents' educational levels and occupations had also been registered, a two-generation pattern of family achievement could be derived which was so pointed that it might well have been predictive of the sample children's present IQ scores. The variables in Table II are all significant at $p < 0.01$.

The two IQ groups were then further subdivided for more detailed comparison with the environmental variables, to provide a matrix of their rela-

TABLE II

Percent High and Moderate IQ among the variables used to measure socio-economic status

Variable	High IQ (141+) n = 82	Moderate IQ (100–140) n = 128
Mother's high level occupation	57	27
Father's high level occupation	78	47
Mother's high level education	50	22
Father's high level education	50	30
Paternal grandfather's high level occupation	43	31
Paternal grandmother's high level occupation	20	8
Maternal grandfather's high level occupation	43	23
Maternal grandmother's high level occupation	18	11
High standard accommodation	49	42
Superior neighbourhood	82	60

tionships. It was clear that the more alike the children's environments, the more alike their IQ scores. This evidence of an association between environment and IQ scores was not a complete surprise, but a more interesting picture emerged when the environments of the 23 children who had scored above IQ 160 were compared with those of the 102 children who had scored below, down to IQ 121. The results are shown graphically in Figure 1.

At this high IQ level there seems to be a distinct change in the children's home backgrounds along the IQ range of 131 to 150. The children entering this top 3% of the Stanford-Binet scale had come from homes which were educationally much more positive than the others and, judging by their exceptionally high IQ scores, seemed to have profited well by it.

IQ scores and even percentiles

Coming back to the question of potential and its fulfilment: there was a noticeable gap for many of the children between the relative levels of their achievements on the Raven's Matrices and Stanford-Binet tests; indications respectively of Fluid and Crystallised intelligence.

Of the 210 sample children, 65 had scored in the top 1 percent of the Raven's test, yet a significant proportion of them had failed to reach that level on the Stanford-Binet. Their mean Stanford-Binet IQ score had been 133 — more like the 95th percentile — right down to around the 85th percentile at 114. The correlation between these two tests is normally good, at around $r = 0.7$, but in this unusual sample, it reached what is probably an all-time low of $r = 0.256$.

FIGURE I
Totals of significant home differences between IQ steps 4-7, where $p < 0.01$

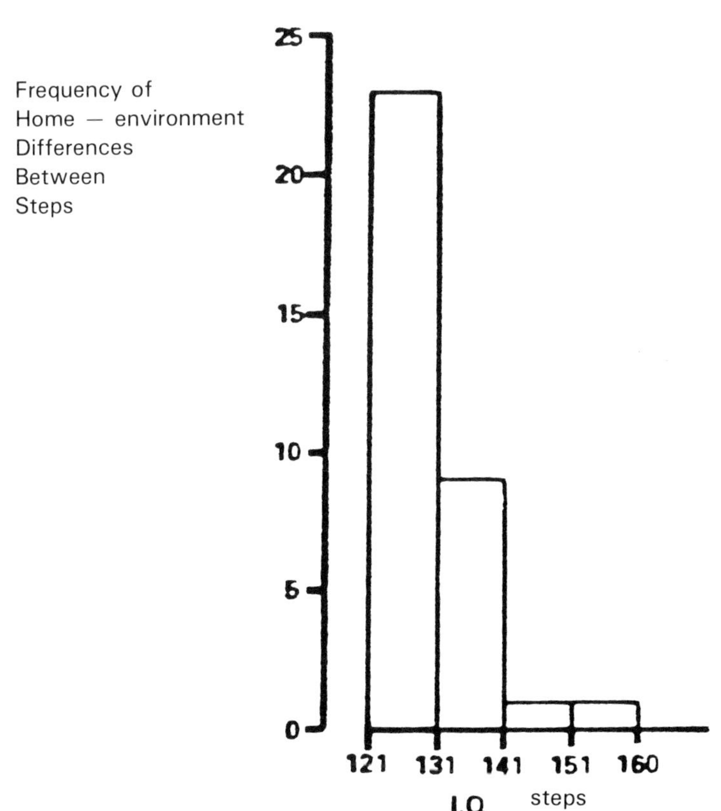

The 187 environmental variables were cumbersome to work with and so they were condensed by a reduction analysis to 11, and named the Constructed Environmental Variables. The 65 top Raven's children were divided into High and Moderate IQ scorers again (of above and below IQ 140), and compared in the light of these composites. Only two clear relationships emerged, but they were highly significant and are shown graphically in Figure 2.

Cultural Milieu (r = 0.503) presented a picture of such matters as music in the home, shared activities, parents' reading habits, hobbies and general concern for the home.

FIGURE 2
Significant Constructed Environmental Variables and IQs of children at the 99th percentile on the Raven's Matrices. n = 65

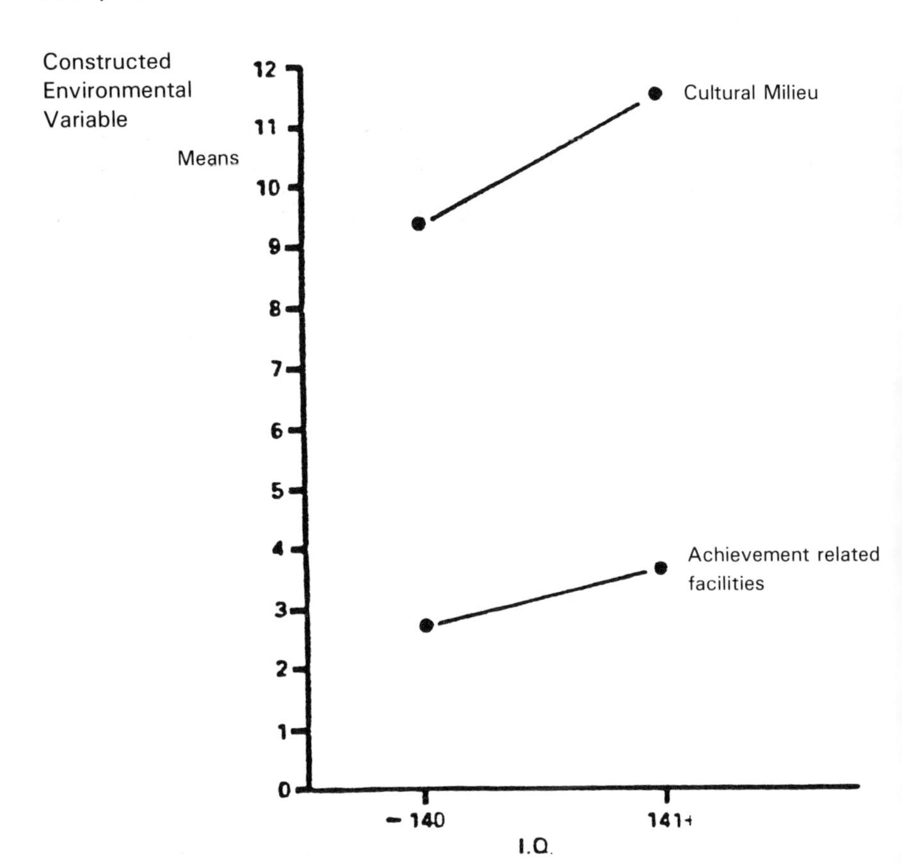

Achievement-Related Facilities (r = 0.433) was a more objective measure of such things as number of books in the house, study space set aside for children, their extra tuition and nursery school attendance.

The children who scored in the top 1 per cent on both the Raven and the Stanford-Binet, that is with similarly developed Fluid and Crystallised intelligences, had these positive family features in significantly greater abundance than those whose Crystallised intelligences were relatively less developed. Neither of these richly influential aspects of family life depend on high socio-economic level or parental expectations for their children or for themselves. They are distinctly practical. This is not to deny the axiom that provision is enabling and poverty is disabling; but rather it is to say that given an adequately secure home base, applied, democratic parenting really seems to add on the IQ points.

Proportional influences

These Constructed Environmental Variables, which were seen to be so productive for the top 1 per cent Raven children, were correlated at r = 0.508 with their IQ scores calculable as an environmental influence of 26 per cent; though doubtless shared with other constitutional influences. For the rest of the sample, however, whose Raven percentiles had varied between 50 and 99, the same Constructed Environmental Variables were correlated at only r = 0.362 with their IQ scores. This indicates a halved environmental influence for the moderately bright children, of 13 per cent. The proportions are shown in Table III.

TABLE III

The significant Constructed Environmental Variables and IQ scores at different Raven's Matrices percentiles

Raven's Percentile	n	Correlation IQ x environmental variables	% environment	% constitution
99+	65	r = 0.508	26	74
50–99	145	r = 0.362	13	87

Discussion

Though the many studies of proportional 'genothreptic' effects (Cattell's word) on intelligence, are not in entire agreement, they do converge roughly at around a 70 per cent heritability and 30 per cent environmental balance (Vernon, 1979). The research presented here appears to have picked up a variation in that balance towards the top of the intellectual ability range. At the highest levels of measured intelligence environmental effects appear to become more pronounced. It would not be unreasonable to say that gifted children are likely to extract greater profit from their life circumstances than less able children.

This evidence, however, does cast some further doubt on the IQ scale as a measure of native ability. Cattell (1980) suggested that Fluid and Crystallised intelligence were somewhat arbitrarily mixed up in the scales and this reinforces his suggestion that for practical purposes the two factors should be distinguished; each to be assessed by measurement on an appropriate 'culture free' or achievement based test. When an IQ score is used to select gifted children, it must be expected that a variable proportion of their environmental opportunities is being sampled too, which is why they are almost always from the educationally most favourable homes.

In this research I had rather hoped to find a golden cut-off point, beyond which children were clearly gifted. But though the IQ scale may be linear, the rest of the children's lives were not, and it vanished like Alice's jar of marmalade. But there was a practical message to come out of all this. There was a noticeable increase in environmental effects from between IQ 130 and IQ 150 and it is suggested that the lower limit be used as a base level, above which the IQ score could be considered more as a measure of achievement. This, along with other non-verbal and specific ability tests would provide the means of identifying about the top 3 per cent of the population.

By sheer weight of numbers, it is clear that the majority of gifted children are neither recognised nor catered for educationally, nor do they break down under the strain of their anonymity. Giftedness is part of a child's life and in normal circumstances the most important influences on its development are largely home based. But from the time a child starts school, new experiences and expectancies should begin to operate. For too many of these exceptional children the key word is still *should.*

References

Adams, B., Ghodsian, M. and Richardson, K. (1976). Evidence for a low upper limit of heritability of mental health performance in a national sample of twins. *Nature,* 263, 314-316.

Cattell, R.B., (1980). *The Scientific Analysis of Personality.* London: Penguin Books.

Cattell, R.B., (1971). *Abilities: Their Structure, Growth and Action.* Boston: Houghton Mifflin.

Cattell, R.B. (1980). The heritability of Fluid, gf, and Crystallised, gc, intelligence, estimated by a least squares use of the MAVA method. *British Journal of Educational Psychology,* 50, 253-265.

Cattell, R.B. and Butcher, H.J. (1968). *The Prediction of Achievement and Creativity.* New York: Bobs-Merrill.
Cattell, R.B. and Cattell, A.K.S. (1960). *The IPAT Culture Fair Intelligence Scales, 1, 2 and 3.* Champaign, Illinois: Institute for Personality and Ability Testing.
Cicourel, A.V., Jennings, K.H., Jennings, S.H.M., Leiter, K.C.W., Mackay, R., Mehan, H. and Roth, D.R., (1974). *Language Use and School Performance.* London: Academic Press.
Clarke, Ann, M. (1980). Comments on heritability. In *A Balance Sheet on Burt* (British Psychological Society, Supplement to the Bulletin), edited by Halla Beloff, 33, 37-38.
Clarke, Ann, and Clark, A.D.B. (1976). *Early Experience: Myth and Evidence.* London: Open Books.
Davie, R. (1982). Child development in context. *Education Section Review* (The British Psychological Society), 6, 4-12.
Davie, R. Butler, N., Goldstein, H. (1972). *From Birth to Seven: A Report of the National Child Development Study.* London: Longmans.
Department of Education and Science, (1977). *Gifted Children in Middle and Comprehensive Schools* London: Her Majesty's Stationery Office.
Douglas, J.B.W. (1968). *All Our Future.* London: Peter Davies.
Freeman, Joan (1979). *The Influence of the Educational Environment on Gifted Children.* Unpublished Ph.D. Thesis: University of Manchester.
Freeman, Joan (1983a). Environment and high IQ: a consideration of Fluid and Crystallised intelligence. *Personality and Individual Differences,* 4, 307-313.
Freeman, Joan (1983b). Emotional problems of the gifted child. *Journal of Child Psychology and Psychiatry,* 24, 481-485.
Jensen, A.R. (1974). Kinship correlations reported by Sir Cyril Burt. *Behaviour Genetics,* 4, 1-28.
Kamin, L.J. (1974). *The Science and Politics of IQ.* London: John Wiley & Sons.
Kline, P. (1980). Burt's false results and modern psychometrics: a comparison. In *A Balance Sheet on Burt* (British Psychological Society, Supplement to the Bulletin), edited by Halla Beloff, 33, 20-23.
Mercer, J. and Lewis, J. (1978). *SOMPA (System of Multicultural Pluralistic Assessment).* New York: the Psychological Corporation.
Ogilvie, E. (1973). *Gifted Children in Primary Schools.* London: Macmillan.
Porter, R.B. and Cattell, R.B. (1959). *Handbook for the Children's Personality Questionnaire.* Champaign, Illinois: Institute for Personality and Ability Testing.
Raven, J.C. (1965). *Guide to Using the Coloured Progressive Matrices.* London: H.K. Lewis.
Stott, D.A. (1967) *Systematic Interview Guides Manual.* London: University of London Press.
Terman, L.M. (1925). *Mental and Physical Traits of a Thousand Gifted Children.* California: Stanford University Press.
Terman, L.M. and Merrill, M.A. (1961). *Stanford-Binet Intelligence Scale. Manual for the Third Revision. Third Revision Form L-M.* London: Harrap.
Vernon, P.E. (1979). *Intelligence: Heredity and Environment.* San Francisco: W.H. Freeman & Co.

The Exceptional Child in the Family

R.M.C. HUNTLEY
Department of Developmental Paediatrics, The Wolfson Centre, Institute of Child Health, London

My interest in this topic — the exceptional child in the family — derives from two separate but linked sources. An earlier period of research into the inheritance of normal human characteristics (Huntley, 1966), carried out in the Medical Research Council's Clinical Genetics Research Unit, was followed by clinical work at The Wolfson Centre in the assessment and management of handicapped children. Amongst these were some for whom the earlier theories and findings seemed to have a direct relevance and application. I am always grateful to John Fraser Roberts, Cedric Carter and Kenneth Holt for introducing me to both these experiences.

Introduction

Most of the children who come to The Wolfson Centre for assessment suffer from some severe and obvious disability or combination of such. They may have gross physical deformities; their vision or hearing may be badly impaired or their intelligence very limited and their learning difficulties severe. Whichever it is, though, singly or in combination, there is no question but that they are severely handicapped, clearly different from everyone else in their immediate family and the environment in which they live. It is no surprise if, because of all their difficulties, there are considerable attendant social and emotional problems for the child and his brothers and sisters and for his parents as he grows up in this particular family.

Not all the children we see, though, are so clearly handicapped and different from their close relatives. Some do not appear handicapped at all. They are sound in body and mind. Neurologically they are functioning normally. Their hearing and vision are perfect. They seem in fact perfectly ordinary normal boys and girls. Yet they have a problem. The problem arises not because they are in any absolute sense physically or mentally handicapped but simply because they are *different.* Different, that is, from the rest of the family in some way which makes them stand out from it, however unobvious this may be at first. They, as it were, 'suffer from comparisons' with the rest of the family and this is the psychological, social, educational and emotional problem they present.

These are, then, the exceptional children in a family. Perhaps the very intelligent child in an otherwise average family, or the very dull child in such a family. Or the child of average ability who by comparison with his much more intelligent siblings and parents falls far short of their expectations of him. In his parents' eyes he is *merely* average, and therefore, by implication, good for what? In another family, perhaps a poor and deprived working-class household, the child of good average ability might stand out from the rest of the family and their social and cultural environment, simply because he is relatively more able than *they* are. Many examples of these 'Able Misfits' are found in Kellmer Pringle (1970).

The question that then arises is how widespread is this *exceptionality* in families? How often do children appear who do not fit comfortably into their families? What causes this? What makes these 'silk purse' and 'sow's ear' children appear in families and then stick out like sore thumbs? What problems arise and what can be done to alleviate them?

Variation Within Families

First, then, the range of ability that can occur within families. An indication of this range can be obtained from correlation coefficients between groups of close relatives – ordinary sibling brothers and sisters and between parents and their children. Results from many different studies show that the correlations for intelligence between these two types of relatives vary around an average of about 0.50 (Erlenmeyer-Kimling, 1963). A sibling or parent-offspring correlation of 0.50 suggests that brothers and sisters within a family tend to show a greater likeness than do unrelated children, whilst still differing quite markedly amongst themselves. If they are half-alike they are also half different. Similarly the offspring as a group will show some general resemblance to both their parents, but individuals may nevertheless vary considerably around the average of the two parents.

Given the distribution of intelligence test scores in the population and given the correlation between siblings it is a straightforward matter to estimate the differences to be expected between children within a family. Let us suppose that Figure 1 shows a typical normal distribution of intelligence in the population as measured by a well-standardised test with a standard deviation of 17 points of IQ and variance (its square) of 289. There is a 68 per cent or 2 in 3 chance that the IQs of any two individuals taken at random from the population will be within 34 points of each other and a 95 per cent chance that they will not differ by more than 68 points. However, there is still a small 5 per cent or 1 in 20 chance that the difference will be more than 68 points. Now if instead of comparing pairs or groups of individuals we compare siblings – ordinary brothers and sisters – and find there is a correlation of 0.50 between them, this means that the variance within these groups has been reduced

FIGURE I
Variation in IQ within sibships if population standard deviation is 17 and correlation between siblings is 0.50.

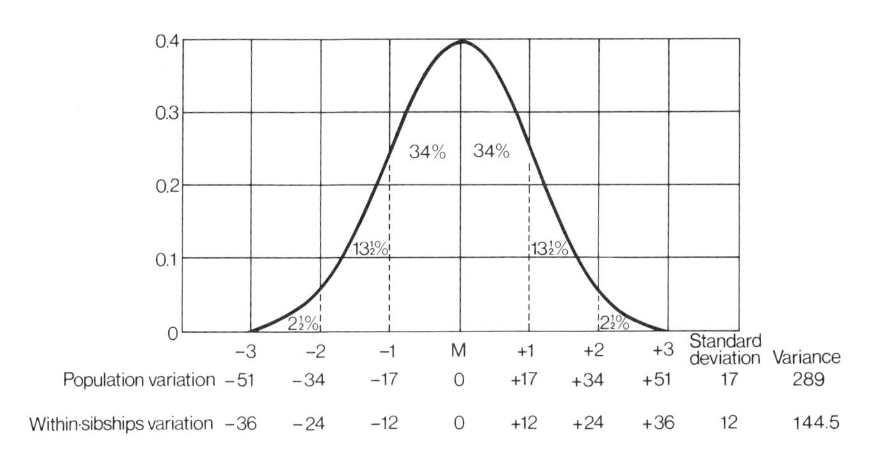

TABLE I

Distribution of maximum differences of IQ within families of four or more children

Maximum difference of IQ	Number of families	Cumulative percentage
60+	2	100
50-59	3	99
40-49	8	94
30-39	19	86
20-29	37	64
10-19	17	23
0- 9	4	4
	90	

Median maximum difference = 26 pts IQ
(Adapted from Maxwell, 1969)

to half that of the population variance and the standard deviation accordingly to the square root of the reduced variance — 12.0. So in this case within family groups there is a quite strong likelihood (68 per cent) that the differences in IQ between siblings will not be more than 24 points of IQ. There is an even greater chance (95 per cent) that two siblings will not differ by more than 48 points of IQ. But there are still five chances in a hundred — a 1 in 20 chance — that the difference in IQ between two sibs in a family could be more than 48 points of IQ. A small chance but one that can and sometimes will occur. Empirical verification of this statistical hypothesis is found in data from a follow-up of the 1947 Scottish Survey (Maxwell, 1969).

All the younger brothers and sisters of the original 1947 sample of children tested were tested as near to their eleventh birthday as possible, individually with the Stanford-Binet Intelligence Scale (Terman and Merrill 1961). The testing began in 1947 and continued for the next sixteen years by which time 1554 younger siblings had been tested. Table I shows the distribution of maximum differences of IQ within 90 of the families all of whom had 4 or more children. As will be seen from the Table the actual proportion of families showing the different maximum differences of IQ bears a close resemblance to the earlier theoretical predictions. 58 of the families, or about two-thirds (64 per cent), show differences of not more than 29 points. But in 5 families (6 per cent) there were maximum differences of over 50 points between the most and least intelligent children in the family. If, for example, 3 of the children in a family had IQs around 125 and the fourth an IQ of 70, it is not difficult to imagine how that particular child could be the 'odd-one-out', or exceptional child in that family and have difficulty in coping with all that was expected of him.

There is, then, a small percentage of families, about 5 per cent and more likely to be those with several children, in which the difference between one child and another in the family could be in excess of 50 points of IQ, with all the other differences that might be associated with that difference, in abilities, aptitudes, schooling, interests, friends and, indeed, future prospects and employment.

Causes of Variability Within Families

Thus there are resemblances within families but also differences. Siblings may be more alike than are unrelated children but they can, as we all know and have seen here, be very different from one another also. There may be a family likeness but they still also differ in appearance, physique, interests, personality and intelligence. What causes this variability in families? What factors underlie the situation where in some families all the children are of much the same level of intelligence, low, high or average, while in others there is a large and continuous range, and in a few there may be a mixture of both, with the majority of the brothers and sisters lying within a narrow range, but perhaps just one being very different from the rest?

The relative *resemblances* could be due to common factors in the environment within the home, but the *differences* are more difficult to explain on an environmental theory. However equally they are treated the children remain stubbornly different. To quote James Maxwell (1969) again, and in regard to one of the Scottish survey families in which the 3 children had IQs of 144, 116 and 82 he asks:

> 'Is this family providing a 'good' environment such that one member attains an IQ of 144, or is it a 'poor' home such that one member only attains an IQ of 82, or is it a 'slightly above average' home so that one member attains an IQ of 116? It is the same home for all three members but there is a difference of 62 points of IQ within the home . . . differences *between* families can in part be accounted for in terms of the social and cultural level of the home, but it is not easy to see how the differences in IQ *within* the same home can be accounted for in terms of different home conditions. Life within the same family is as near as we can get to uniform social and cultural conditions' (p.183).

He concludes that the outstanding feature of the sib testing evidence (in the Scottish survey) was 'the great variability of IQ within relatively homogeneous environmental conditions' (p.183).

So it is similarities we would expect within families in intelligence if environmental factors are predominant, but it is differences that in fact we are more likely to get. A genetic hypothesis seems more applicable to account for this variability; and not only the variability of the siblings themselves but its concentration around the average of the two parents' intelligence. Each child inherits half his genes from his father and half from his mother. So genetically they are all half like each parent. But which particular half of each parent's genes a child inherits is a matter of chance. So one child of, say, a very intelligent father may receive the half that contributed most to the father's high intelligence and, depending on the other half that he inherits from his mother, could be as intelligent or even more intelligent than his father. Another child might be less fortunate and receive the other half of the father's genes including only few of those which contributed to the father's high ability. In his case, again depending on the contribution from his mother, he could be of near average ability. In most cases, of course, the children will receive a more varied mixture of their parents' genes — some which will have contributed to their high intelligence and some to making them more average. Consequently, to the extent that it is hereditary, the average level of intelligence of the children in a family will tend to be the average of their parents' intelligence. Thus, if the father's IQ is 100 and the mother's

80, their children will show a range of ability around the mid-parent IQ of 90. If father's IQ is 120 and mother's is 140, then the children's IQ will vary around 130.

The extent of the variation in a family, as we have seen, is considerable. Sometimes it can be more than 50 points of IQ. Thus occasionally a very bright child will appear in a generally very average family and sometimes one child will be relatively dull in an otherwise very high-powered, high-achieving professional family. This can sometimes cause problems. The exceptional child in a family, be he the relatively bright one or the relatively dull one, compared with the others, can have very different interests, attitudes and friends. Unless there is understanding and tolerance and acceptance of him for what he is rather than what his parents would like or expect him to be, he can have a very difficult time in growing up. Perhaps the genetic hypothesis advanced in this section is best summed up by a letter published in The Times during the nature-nurture controversy that raged through its columns some while ago. The correspondent wrote modestly of his own 'undistinguished career befitting a person of quite average intelligence' compared with that of his brother, 'a man of outstanding intelligence and a distinguished engineer', and asked:

> 'Am I average and was he brilliant because he inherited superior genes, or did my indifferent IQ arise from 'social institutions and structures'? If the latter how does this arise? We lived in the same home, went to the same grammar school and both received the same devoted and impartial love and care from our parents'.

The Exceptional Children who become a Family Problem

It would be wrong to suggest that all children who are at the extreme end of the family 'range' of intelligence are potentially 'problem' children. Clearly large differences between children in a family need not be a problem. Most parents can accept and cope with children who are very different from their other children and themselves, and accept them for what they are. A few though, evidently, have certain expectations of what a child, specifically *their* child, should be like, and cannot easily accommodate themselves to any appreciable deviation from this norm, however unalterable this may be. A number of these exceptional or 'odd-man-out' children have been seen over the years at The Wolfson Centre. They present as a problem in that they are not making what is considered to be satisfactory progress in school. They are referred for assessment of their difficulties and advice on how they can be helped.

Characteristics of the exceptional child

On comparing the case-notes of these so called 'educational failure' children, one is struck by the number of features they have in common.

For example, there is a group who showed the following characteristics:

(1) They were not as a whole, measuring up to their parents' and often their school's expectations of them.

(2) They were predominantly boys. Of 37 identified as being different from the rest of the family, all but 3 were boys and in the 12 I myself saw and followed up there were no girls.

(3) The 12 boys at the time of assessment ranged in age between 6 and 12 years, with a mean age of 9 years 7 months. Their mean IQ was 100.5 with a range from 90 to 114. So this group were all of average intelligence relative to the whole population.

(4) Most of them were significantly behind their mental age in educational attainments. (3 were delayed in both reading and arithmetic, 3 in reading only and one in arithmetic only. However 5 of the 12 did not show any delay in attainments of more than 12 months).

(5) Relative to their general level of intellectual development all these children had a good vocabulary.

(6) They were typically delightful children, friendly, polite and sociable. Most were quite lively and talkative; some were quiet, serious and apparently thoughtful. It came as quite a surprise to find for example that they did not know how many days there were in a week, or how many pence in a pound. Even so they tended to be puzzled as to why they had come! A typical school report would be: 'He is socially up to and beyond his age group, but academic perfor mance is still not very good'.

(7) The medical examination rarely showed any physical abnormalities. The children were neurolgically sound and generally in good robust health. In one or two cases there was a suggestion of slight but very minimal clumsiness.

(8) Virtually all the boys considered here were attending private preparatory schools, some with very high academic standards and expectations. Some would have started at state primary schools but had been transferred to the private sector because of unacceptably slow progress in the state school. The hope would have been that the smaller classes and individual help in the private school would help and benefit them.

(9) The 12 boys had other brothers and sisters, all of whom seemed by report to be brighter and livelier than this, their failing brother. The older siblings were at selective schools or university; the younger, often it seemed, a girl, might at five years of age be already reading better than her brother was at nine.

(10) Their parents were nearly always professional people — company director, surgeon, army officer etc. — and their children were all under 'strong pressure to succeed' both at home and in school.

In summary, then, there seem to be particular family situations in which certain children can appear to have special learning difficulties or other problems. This is not through any fault of their own but simply because they are *that* child in *that* family and diverge from its normal pattern to a greater extent than can be accommodated in that family. The child being discussed here seems most likely to be a boy, in the junior school range and at a private preparatory school. He is the son of professional parents, is of good physique and healthy. He is friendly polite and likeable and has an intelligence in the average range. But he has difficulty in keeping up in school and his attainments tend to lag behind his capacity. He is under considerable pressure, actual, implied or inferred, to succeed in the manner his older siblings have done, and his younger ones seem highly likely to do.

Management of the problem

The problem is therefore not just confined to the child; the whole family is affected and needs help and advice. It seems necessary to make clear to them that there is nothing fundamentally wrong or backward with their son, nor is he lazy or obstructive, rather that he just happens to be different from his siblings and from the general family pattern and expectations. This is not his parents' fault or doing. There is a range of intellectual capacity and functioning in a family and in his case he might be one of the extreme forms of this variation. He has to be accepted for what he is. He needs to be praised and encouraged for what he *can* do, and not pressed to perform beyond his capacity. This would be fruitless and is more likely to make the boy give up in despair and do even less well than he might otherwise do. It may be that the school he is attending is too demanding, and we would hope to be able to suggest others which might be more congenial and suitable for him. Above all he must not be allowed to 'suffer from comparisons' with his own brothers and sisters.

Later development

Most of the group of children referred to above were seen several years ago and are now grown up. It seemed important to discover what in fact happened to them following their assessment and the advice given. Did they win through the years and find satisfactory and appropriate careers? Did the family take to heart the advice given and modify their attitude and feelings about their exceptional child and their expectations of him? With undue pressure taken off them, did the children make better progress in school?

We wrote to the families to find out what had happened. Some had moved away and were untraceable, but most replied. They seemed pleased to have re-established contact and on the whole reported satisfactory outcomes for their sons. I should like to give one example of a family in which there were all the ingredients of a situation which could cause difficulties for one child in the family, but where with understanding and tolerance on all sides the problems seemed to happily resolve.

Stephen

Stephen was a delightful little boy, friendly, ginger-haired and freckled. His IQ at 10½ years was in the low 90's. He had no special difficulties, but his older and much brighter sisters made him appear slow to his professional parents. It was noted that he showed mild anxiety in answering questions verbally but was relaxed and confident with non-verbal 'performance' type tasks. An explanation, as we saw it, and advice were given along the lines detailed above. A small non-academic boarding school was considered for Stephen but he did not wish to go away from home and instead attended the local comprehensive school. Some years later in a very informative letter his father told us that Stephen did not do well academically, but was remarkably skillful with his hands. He did all the household repairs, enjoyed working with metals and was intensely interested in carrying out motor car repairs and maintenance. On leaving school at 17 he became a trainee dental technician. He did not enjoy the theoretical part of the work but persevered at it. But he thoroughly enjoyed the practical part of the training and produced work of a very high standard. Stephen was well aware that he was different from his very intelligent sisters both of whom are now doctors, but this caused him no worries and there was never any friction at home. He was a remarkably well-adjusted young man, happy and kind, and extremely popular at school, in the hospital and in the neighbourhood in which they lived. Stephen, then, and others like him, was a normal healthy child of average ability, but exceptional because he was born into a family which as a whole was much above the population average in intelligence. His divergence from the family pattern was such that he became a puzzle and a 'problem' in that family, and the parents needed help in understanding and resolving it.

It seems clear that once they are accepted for what they are, and not pressed to achieve beyond their relatively limited capacity, such children can make progress and fulfil themselves in congenial work later on. Stephen was an example of the child who is exceptional because he is of only average ability in a family of high ability. I should like to conclude with an example of another boy who suffered from the other kind of comparison — he was the very intelligent boy in what seemed otherwise to be a more ordinary and average kind of family.

John

John was referred to us because of sleeplessness and not getting on well at school. He was first seen at the age of seven. His trouble seemed to arise from his being big, clumsy, clever and young. On the Stanford-Binet Intelligence Scale his IQ was 147. So, at seven he had the intellectual development of a child of nearly eleven. It seemed to us unlikely that his relatively poor attainments were due to lack of sleep, but that he probably didn't need as much as many seven year old. It seemed more likely that he was not getting enough to do in school, or much encouragement at home. Although basically very bright and tall and over seven years old he was still, because of his date of birth, in the Infant part of the school with much younger children. Yet some of the items he tackled successfully in the testing were at a 14 year old level 'This is the sort of thing I like doing' he would comment. At home he certainly seemed to be the odd one out, and to receive little sympathy from either parent. His father was very strict with him and was continually comparing him unfavourably with his older brother, telling him he couldn't do any of the things his brother could do at his age, and that his brother was a 'real boy'. John's mother also found it difficut to accept his divergence from the family pattern. He was a gentle child and preferred girls company to boys, and this worried her. She also said that he was very disobedient. he went to bed early but didn't go to sleep till 11 o'clock. Then she discovered that he read in bed. He had been told not to, but went on doing so. She often found books hidden under the mattress. She said: 'Children should do as they are told . . . we had no trouble like this with my older boy'. The parents did not seem to do much to encourage or support possible interests John had. They had moved out of the city into the country within the past year but had seen little of the countryside around them. John never went shopping with his mother; he preferred to stay at home as he had few needs and no interest in money. His mother did not know where the public library was. Yet John was extremely interested in reading, particularly a book on astronomy which his grandfather had given him. He remembered and quoted from it. John loved writing stories and he composed a very beautiful short story for his mother. He had put a great deal of effort into it and thought it the best story he had ever written. When he gave it to her she took one look at it and said that his writing was appalling and she did not wonder that he got into trouble at school. He had not written for her again. He did, however, continue to write stories and make them up, but kept them to himself. At school also John's high and creative ability seemed to be undervalued. We have examples of good, imaginative and well-illustrated stories he had written with comments like 'Your stories are often interesting but your handwriting is so confused that the work is difficult to read. Rewrite, please' and again, 'This is a good story, but your handwriting is disgraceful'. And as if all this weren't enough, John was not popular at school. He had only one friend, but he lived some distance away, and they seldom met.

This, then, seemed another kind of 'exceptional child in the family'. An intelligent, imaginative but very lonely boy, at odds with his family, failing in school and showing considerable social and emotional problems. The situation as we saw it was explained to John's mother. Children within a family differed very much. John was a clever boy with his own imaginative interests and he needed sympathetic understanding and encouragement in the things he was interested in and good at. It was uncertain how willing or able John's parents might be to change their attitude towards him, and the way they were bringing him up. So it was important to ensure that he was at least understood by his school teachers. We visited the school, discussed our findings with them and it was felt that they would do their best to help him and allow his imagination full play without too much inhibiting emphasis on his spelling and writing. He was seen for review a year and two years later, when for the first time his father came as well. He was then nine and a half. His intelligence continued high and his attainments shot up. In two years his reading made six and a half years progress to over a 13 year level and his arithmetic also rose from a 10 to a 15 year level. Some of the family problems had been resolved. His mother was showing her interest and concern for John by attending an evening class on the development of personality!

It has been possible to check John's progress from time to time. He has continued to fulfil his early intellectual promise, often to other people's surprise. In the secondary school, when he was about 12, he chose as a subject for a project 'Spiritualism, Immortality and Reincarnation'. His teacher returned it with the comment 'I expected the worst when I saw the title of this, expecting a broth of exorcists, ouijas and poltergeists. In fact the maturity and wisdom with which you discuss this are quite extraordinary. It is quite outstanding'. John took and passed 3 A-level examinations, though with not very good grades. When I last enquired he was 19 and had completed one year at University, reading Economics, English and Sociology. He wants to be a Social Worker. This then is a further, extended example of a child who, because by chance he diverged so much from his own family's concept of the normal, developed into a truly handicapped child with complex social, educational and emotional problems.

In such cases a full and comprehensive assessment of the child and his family is required and much discussion and counselling with the family may be needed to help them accept fully their 'exceptional child' and allow him to develop in his own particular and individual way.

References

Erlenmeyer-Kimling, L. and Jarvik, L.F. (1963). Genetics and intelligence: a review. *Science,* 142, 1477.

Huntley, R.M.C. (1966). Heritability of intelligence. In *Genetic and Environmental Factors in Human Ability,* edited by J.E. Meade and A.S. Parkes (Eugenics Society Symposium Volume No.4). Edinburgh and London: Oliver & Boyd.

Maxwell, J. (1969). *Sixteen Years On: A Follow-Up of the 1941 Scottish Survey.* London: University of London Press for the Scottish Council for Research in Education.

Pringle, M.L.K. (1970). *Able Misfits.* London: Longman Group.

Terman, L.M. and Merrill, M.A. (1961). *Stanford-Binet Intelligence Scale.* London: Harrap & Co.

Index

THE BIOLOGY OF INTELLIGENCE (Symposium 1983)